Coca-Cola®
Collectible
Bean Bags & Plush

Coca-Cola®
Collectible
Bean Bags & Plush

LINDA LEE HARRY

BECKETT PUBLICATIONS

Book design by Sara Maneval.

Published by:
Beckett Publications
15850 Dallas Parkway
Dallas, Texas 75248

ISBN: 1-887432-97-3
Beckett™ is a registered trademark of Beckett Publications

First Edition: September 2000
Beckett Corporate Sales and Information (972) 991-6657

The contributors to this publication have attempted to place current fair market value on each collectible. This book is to be used as a guide only. Prices in this guide reflect current market rates determined just prior to printing. Prices are based on a grading system of 1–10 (with 10 being Mint and 1 being poor). All bean bags and plush shown are in Mint condition unless stated otherwise. As always, items are only worth what someone is willing to pay for them. Auction and dealer prices will vary based on condition, geographic location and demand. Neither the Authors nor the Publisher assumes responsibility for any losses that might be incurred through the sale or purchase of merchandise because of the information contained herein.

Printed in Canada

Contents

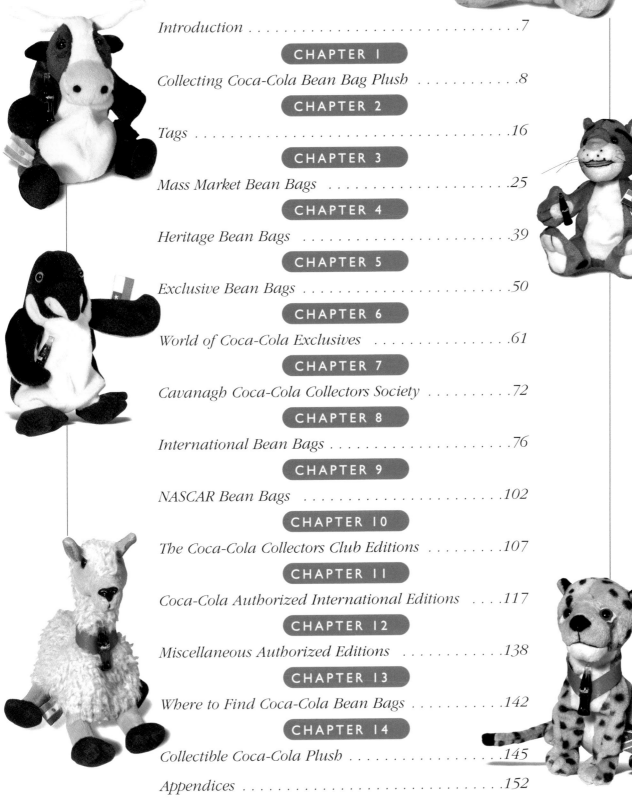

About the Author

Linda Lee Harry spent several years working in mission hospitals in Korea and Thailand, collecting Coca-Cola bottles from the many places she visited. Then, while working in a hospital lab in Oregon, she was chemically poisoned, severely damaging her immune system. Friends brought Coke bottles from around the world to brighten long hospital stays in isolation.

Soon, Linda's collection filled several rooms. Collecting Coca-Cola memorabilia became the family hobby and respite through many difficult years of recovery. When times were hard, Linda reluctantly sold some of the collection. Her sister, Suzi Harry, built a Website to show Linda's unique Coca-Cola pieces. The site remains today, carrying a full line of Coca-Cola collectibles and specialty bean bag plush.

Acknowledgments

I am grateful to all our bean bag plush customers who constantly send me hot tips and new information, fueling our passion to collect Coca-Cola bean bags. I am indebted to those who happily shared their collections and excitement in the writing of this book: David Zimmerman, Judith Miller, Sherry McCullough, Selina Wan, William Paul and Jean Gibbs-Simpson.

I can't thank George Parker at World of Coca-Cola Atlanta enough for all his help and insight in tracking down information about special bean bags. Thanks goes to Jennifer Hicks at Cavanagh Group International for getting us the latest scoop as she tries to keep our orders straight.

The editors also wish to thank Jim Hollister, Kathy Scales, Dee Dukes and John Cavanagh for supplying timely information and many of the photos in this book.

My deepest thanks go to my sisters, Suzi Harry and Sandra Silvius, for their constant encouragement and willingness to shoulder the office work so I could have time to write. They are always giving, loving and willing to cheer me on. Without their enthusiastic support, this book never would have been a reality. And I am most thankful for my parents, Bill and Margaret Harry, who taught me to trust God is working all things out for my good. You are my heroes.

Introduction

One bright summer's day my sister brought me a cuddly white polar bear with a big smile. I instantly fell in love. As a Coca-Cola collector for years, I was delighted to find that The Coca-Cola Company made bean bag plush.

The little bear sat on my computer for months, attracting many comments from passers by. Friends then gave me a seal and another polar bear as Christmas gifts. I had no idea there were more and immediately began hunting for them all.

Finding these adorable little guys proved to be a hit-and-miss proposition. While getting a Coke at a local convenience store, I spied a big orange box filled with three editions. On closer inspection, I found they were made by Cavanagh Group International in Georgia, but I didn't have any more information on the manufacturer.

Then our Coca-Cola collectibles Webstore began receiving dozens of requests for Coca-Cola brand bean bags. My sisters and I filled our store with polar bears and seals that quickly sold out.

Our days are now spent tracking down rarer editions from around the world. We've tried to learn everything possible about bean bags, and in the process, we've met some of the nicest people on earth: Coca-Cola collectors. It is always fun to share what we've learned with you.

CHAPTER 1

Collecting Coca-Cola Bean Bag Plush

"Things go better with Coke"
— 1963 slogan

1996 TELEVISION COMMERCIAL: "POLAR BEAR/BABY SEAL"

What do you get when you put together the most recognizable trademark in the world, Coca-Cola, and the top collecting passion, bean bag plush? One of the hotter collectibles on the planet!

Coca-Cola brand bean bag plush is a dream come true for many collectors. From the cuddly polar bears to the huggable seals to the adorable reindeer, these North Pole stars of everyone's favorite television commercials have taken the country by storm.

They pop up in supermarkets, national retail chain stores, gift and collectibles shops — even in restaurant promotions.

To the delight of children and adults alike, the collection has grown from the original six lovable characters to more than two hundred editions in just three years. But finding Coca-Cola brand bean bag toys always has been a challenge.

In recognition of the growing passion for Coca-Cola brand bean bag plush, The Coca-Cola Company authorized this book, filled with interesting stories and exclusive insider information on these popular collectibles. You'll learn how Coca-Cola bean bags are made and what makes them so collectible.

See photographs and read facts about every authorized Coca-Cola brand bean bag plush made. Get tips on where to find your favorite North Pole friends. Look at actual tag examples, along with variations, so you'll know the real deal from a bean bag imposter. Even take a sneak peak at upcoming editions.

And in the process, hopefully, you'll spend many entertaining hours becoming a Coke bean bag aficionado.

In 1997, as the beanie bag craze was becoming a full-fledged national phenomenon, Coca-Cola granted a license to Cavanagh Group International (CGI) to produce its brand of bean bag plush characters.

Headquartered just outside Atlanta, CGI produces and distributes a wide variety of Coca-Cola licensed merchandise. From ornaments to resin figures, cookie jars to fine porcelain buildings, plush polar bears to musical snowglobes, CGI has been responding to collectors' needs for the past ten years.

AN INSTANT LOVE AFFAIR

When one of the most successful television advertising campaigns debuted, the Coca-Cola polar bear became a dazzling superstar. So it seemed a natural for the first bean bag plush characters to be polar bears and seals.

Just like the ads, they were an instant hit. Children and adults alike fell in love with Coca-Cola brand bean bag plush characters, snapping them up for toys and presents.

Recognizing their popularity, Coca-Cola trademarked the design of the polar bear, and soon after, the seal. Their whimsical smiles and charming plush design, not to mention their miniature bottles of Coke, made spotting —and buying — these bears and seals an easy task for collectors.

Additional polar characters were added to the line: reindeer, walrus, husky, penguin, killer whale. Even a can of Coke with sunglasses joined the Coca-Cola bean bag collection. Still, every set revolves around the polar bears and seals, the most popular characters.

WHO COLLECTS COKE BEAN BAGS?

Although first designed to be a child's toy, collectors quickly recognized the potential value of these warm, fuzzy characters. The passion for collecting isn't limited to age, gender, occupation or region, consuming everyone from housewives to business leaders to teenagers to retirees. The bean bag's universal appeal is evident by the growing number of international editions popping up around the world. England, Germany, Australia, New Zealand, Canada and Hong Kong all lay claim to special Coca-Cola bean bags.

Thanks to the World Wide Web, collectors from anywhere can go to Internet sites offering Coca-Cola bean bag plush for sale, trade or auction.

The number of editions now available allows hobbyists the option of specializing their collection. Some collect only polar bears or seals. Others want only exclusive editions. Paired girl-boy bean bags are very popular, as are themed sets such as the sports and NASCAR bean bags.

Think you're too late to get into Coca-Cola brand bean bag plush collecting? Think again. New sets are released

LION BEAN BAG
SHOWING PELLET
FILLING

VARIATIONS ON A REINDEER THEME

every year, and picking up the latest line is a great way to start. Almost all the editions produced since 1997 are still available at reasonable prices. So start collecting now. Collect because you never know how much they will be worth in the future. But, most of all, collect for the fun of it!

WHAT MAKES COCA-COLA BRAND BEAN BAG PLUSH SO COLLECTIBLE?

There are practically as many answers to that question as there are collectors. The increasing popularity of the Coca-Cola bean bags is fueled by many factors:

- *The Coca-Cola Name.* Loyal fans of Coca-Cola make up one of the largest groups of collectors. It seems only natu-

ral that Coca-Cola would put its name on one of the hottest trends: bean bag plush.

- *Cuteness.* From the smiling face of the polar bear to the whimsical whiskers on the seal, just about everyone falls in love with these favorite polar characters. Just looking at them makes you happy.

- *Affordably Priced.* Who can resist these lovable toys when most retail between $6 and $10? And at those prices, who needs to? From a child's toy to a serious collector's prize, Coca-Cola brand bean bag plush is priced so everyone can afford to collect.

- *Tags.* Collectors love the "swing tag" on each Coca-Cola bean bag character which

PUTTING A NEW FACE ON POLAR BEARS

gives the tag number and name. Tag numbers make collecting easy.

- *Scarcity.* Because Coca-Cola brand bean bag plush toys are marketed in many different ways, it can be difficult to find all that have been produced. Half the fun is the hunting for new editions or finding that special retired bean bag to complete a collection.

- *Internet.* With one click, collectors are no longer limited to what is available in their area. Bean bags from a promotion in Germany show up almost instantly for sale to everyone around the world. Auction sites abound with Coca-Cola brand bean bag plush causing frenzied bidding wars. Whether for information, purchase, trading or just for fun, the Internet has added a new dimension to collecting.

- *Increasing Value.* Knowing that each bean bag is produced in limited numbers and will only be available for a short time keeps values high. The success of these cuddly toys is seen on the secondary market, where retired and exclusive edition bean bags continue to grow in value.

WHAT MAKES IT A BEAN BAG?

Stuffing? Size? Tags?

Coca-Cola brand bean bag plush is cut from a plush pattern, sewn, then partially filled with small round pellets. Because the bean bags are only partially filled, they have a playful floppiness.

Faces and paws are filled with polyester fibers to maintain their shape. Plastic eyes and noses are affixed and mouths stitched. Finally, clothing and accessories are added, and that famous Coca-Cola bottle is affixed to the paw using a bolting mechanism.

With few exceptions, Cavanagh has kept the size of the bean bag plush a consistent six inches tall. The most notable exception to this is the 1997 Musicland/Media Play Exclusive #0113 Bear with Long Stocking Cap, which is taller than most at eight inches. Bean bags in the new line of mini-collectibles, introduced in 1999, are four inches high.

All Coca-Cola brand bean bag plush produced by CGI have the distinctive bottle cap swing tag. While other lines of plush toys may carry the Coca-Cola name, you can always identify the familiar silver and red swing tag on any Coca-Cola bean bag animal. (More information about swing tags is found in Chapter 2.)

Style# 0104
COCA-COLA Polocr
Bear in Snowflake Cap
The original
Coca-Cola® brand
Bean Bag Plush
brings your favorite
North Pole characters
to life in adorable
bean bag plush.

VARIATIONS — A COLLECTOR'S DREAM

While trademark shapes keep the Coca-Cola brand bean bag plush remarkably uniform, some variations have occurred. A variation can be everything from a mistagged bean bag, a misspelled word, a missing accessory piece or an intentional design change. Variations quickly become the most valuable editions because they are so rare.

Mistags — Why does your Seal in a Red Tee Shirt have a tag that states it's a Polar Bear with Pink Bow? It is a mistag, a mistake made during production.

Mistagged bean bags occurred more frequently in the first two sets, but they pop up from time to time and are highly prized by collectors.

Spelling errors — All bean bags go through a rigorous quality control check at several stages, so a spelling mistake rarely slips by. The #0104 Polar Bear in Snowflake Cap showed up as "Polocr Bear" on a few editions and is considered very valuable.

Intentional Changes — In the first set released in the spring of 1997 several changes occurred between the first edition and subsequent production. Differences may be seen on the tag or in accessories.

Style #0109 was first released as "Bear with Bottle," then the tag was changed to "Polar Bear with Bottle" to make the set uniform.

Style #0108 Penguin in Delivery Cap first came out with a plain green delivery cap. A colorful red Coca-Cola button was added to the cap in later production.

Originally dark brown with tan features, the reindeer bean bag took on a different look in 1998. Larger and more playful, the reindeer is light brown and tan with much more detail in the face, large button nose and stitched feet.

The biggest intentional design change occurred in 1999 with the release of the "new face" polar bears. Coca-Cola wanted to make the bean bag bears more like the famous polar bear advertisements.

Changes touched every part of the

famous polar bear bean bag. Faces are thinner, with smaller ears. Eyes now have eyelids. A longer style nose is introduced. The stitching on the mouth is more detailed.

Hands and feet were stitched to give a more realistic look. The addition of a patch of gray fabric to the feet makes them more closely resemble paws. And the famous Coca-Cola contour bottle now rests on the underside of the left paw on most new face editions. "Old face" editions always sported the bottle upright in the right paw.

Collectors rushed to get all the old face editions before they disappeared. Pairs of old face and new face styles remain very popular.

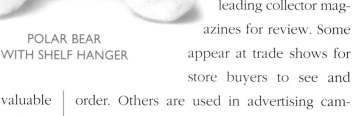

POLAR BEAR
WITH SHELF HANGER

Prototypes — By far the most valuable editions are the first prototypes produced. Changes occur during the approval and manufacturing process so the finished bean bag may be significantly different than the first prototype. To understand prototype variation it is helpful to understand the manufacturing process.

Cavanagh designs new bean bags, then submits line drawings to The Coca-Cola Company for approval. Once approved, a prototype of each bean bag character is produced. Many changes can occur between original idea and final product.

Full production begins with each factory making only one bean bag style from start to finish. At some stages during production pieces are assembled by hand, giving rise to small variations. It can take up to a year from the design stage to the finished product that appears on the shelves of your local retail store.

While production on the new bean bag goes on, CGI begins promoting the new editions. Prototypes are sent to leading collector magazines for review. Some appear at trade shows for store buyers to see and order. Others are used in advertising campaigns and promotions.

Before Cavanagh began production on the first set of bean bags, a prototype set of six was developed in 1996. A few prototype sets were produced for selected distributors to "test the water." No one knew these playful little toys would turn the collecting world upside down.

Although similar to the released version, there are many distinguishing differences.

The prototype set did not have swing tags. Tush tags are dated 1996. The seal has the same plastic nose as the bears. A polar bear had a blue baseball cap in the prototype set. (It is red in the released edition.)

Few prototypes find their way into the hands of collectors and are the most prized. For example, a rare prototype set including the #0111 Polar Bear with Blue Cap recently sold at auction for $625.

A more recent prototype of the Winter 1999 set of six bean bags first showed up in advertising materials with black smudges on the noses of the polar bears. In an attempt to make the polar bears look more realistic, the black smudge came off looking more like dirt and was quickly removed from the line. Only a few prototype sets used for advertising purposes ever appeared with the black, smudged noses. None were ever sold.

PACKAGING CHANGES

Some Coca-Cola brand bean bag plush characters come in factory-sealed plastic bags. Others are fitted with special hooks on their heads called "shelf hangers" to make it easy for stores to display them. The same bean bag may come with more than one version (in bag/not in bag; with hook/no hook) depending on the market to which it is being sold.

It is important to some collectors to keep the bean bag in the exact state in which it is bought. So if it comes in a sealed bag, keep it in the sealed bag. If it has a hook, don't cut it off (unless, of course, you just want to enjoy these as toys). All seals come with their whiskers taped down, but most collectors remove the tape immediately.

CHAPTER 2

Tags

"It's the real thing"
— 1942 slogan

As every collector knows, it's the tag that makes the bean bag so collectible. Each Coca-Cola brand bean bag plush comes with two tags.

ORIGINAL TUSH TAG
FRONT (TOP)
AND CE TUSH TAG
BACK (BOTTOM)

TUSH TAGS

A "tush tag" is sewn into the seams of the bottom. On the front is printed: "'Coca-Cola Plush Design'©(Year). The Coca-Cola Company. All Rights Reserved." The back is printed with the washing instructions, contents and: "Made in China and Reg. No PA-4905(KR)." The copyright year changes according to when the bean bags were made.

Bean bags produced after 1998 now have a large "CE" with the address of CGI in England.

The swing tag, or "hang tag," comes in a book style shaped like a bottle cap and is highly prized by collectors. It is attached to the ear or arm of the bean bag with a plastic strip.

SWING TAG FRONT   SWING TAG BACK

#101 SWING TAG INSIDE BOOK

The bottle cap-shaped tag front states, "Collectible Coca-Cola Brand Bean Bag Plush" and is in the familiar silver and red.

On the inside left of the tag is the style number and "name" of the individual bean bag. Although Coca-Cola brand bean bags do not have names (other than members of the International Collection), each has a description which collectors use to identify the individual bean bag. All state, "The original Coca-Cola brand bean bag plush brings your favorite North Pole characters to life in adorable bean bag plush."

The right side contains the copyright and trademark information.

The back has a warning to remove tag before giving to children, a barcode and "Made in China." Several different barcode numbers have appeared on bean bags through the years. The words, "Distributed by Cavanagh Group International, Roswell, GA, USA" were added to tags in 1998.

Never remove the tags if you are interested in the future value of your Coca-Cola brand bean bag plush. But if your only interest is for a child's toy, by all means cut the swing tag off before giving it to your child.

On some lists of Coca-Cola brand bean bags the letters CS or HS appear before the style number. This refers to the line the bean bag comes from. CS is for "Mass" and specialty bean bags. HS is for "Heritage," or gift store, lines.

Although the swing tag has remained uniform for several years, some special tags have appeared on various Coca-Cola brand bean bag characters.

SPRING 1997 SECOND   YEAR 2000 SET
YELLOW PRICE TAG   SECOND RED TAG

DOUBLE TAGS

Some bean bags come with special second tags identifying something special about the set, a specific retailer or special price tag. Some versions of the Spring 1997 set had a second price tag attached to the swing tag.

Members of the Year 2000 set all have special second red tags marking them proudly as part of an "Exclusive 2000 Design."

The Winter 1999 set sold at Albertson's stores at Christmastime. By special agreement, a second "Albertsons" tag was added to the swing tag. Because Albertson's had recently bought Lucky Markets and Sav-on Drugs, a few bean bags made it to stores with both "Lucky" and "Sav-on" second tags. Most were cut off before distribution.

All Coca-Cola brand bean bag plush sold in Canada must have double tags, one in French and one

ENGLISH AND CANADIAN SWING TAGS SIDE BY SIDE

in English. Both swing tags have identical information other than the language in which they are printed.

When the Manchu Wok Restaurant chain (headquartered in Canada) released the #0177 Polar Bear in Red Satin Jacket, half the bears displayed single English tags and half sported double French/English tags. All had an additional rectangular tag identifying the Manchu Wok restaurant, and collectors rushed to get both English and French/English editions.

(RIGHT) EXCLUSIVE BLOCKBUSTER SWING TAGS WITH TAB

(BOTTOM) INSIDE GCC #0166 SWING TAG

MEDIA PLAY EXCLUSIVE TO US 1998
AND 1999 SWING TAGS

EXCLUSIVE TAGS

Many of the exclusive Coca-Cola bean bags produced for a specific store, event or promotion are marked with exclusive tags. The tag design itself may be different, or the bean bags may have a special second tag. Also, the name of the special bean bag may reflect its exclusive source.

The first set to include exclusive tags (swing tags produced only for one particular store or chain of stores) is the Blockbuster set of 1997. Swing tags from this set have an extra price tab

MANCHU WOK
EXCLUSIVE
SWING TAG

WORLD OF COCA-COLA "E" SWING TAG
AND WORLD OF COCA-COLA EXCLUSIVE
SECOND SWING TAG

($5.99). It was also the first time "Distributed by Cavanagh Group International" appeared on the back of the swing tag.

The special polar bear made for Gift Creation Concepts retailers in 1998 has the words, "A GCC Exclusive" right inside the swing tag after the style number and name.

The Media Play Exclusive winter set of four, released in 1998, carries a second bright orange "Exclusive to Us" tag that is larger than the regular Cavanagh swing tag. The set of three adorable polar bears released in 1999

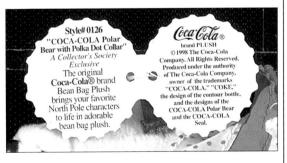

ECC ATLANTA INSIDE AND COLLECTORS
CLASSIC INSIDE SWING TAG
#0126 INSIDE SWING TAG

FRONT OF THE ZOO ATLANTA PANDA
SECOND TAG AND KROGER PANDA
SECOND TAG

for Media Play also have a second "Exclusive to Us" tag in gold.

As mentioned earlier, delightful polar bears in Chinese outfits produced for Manchu Wok restaurants in 1998 carry a special rectangular tag besides the swing tag.

Exclusive bean bags produced for World of Coca-Cola and their Everything Coca-Cola stores in Atlanta, Las Vegas and New York all wear special exclusive tags. First production run of the exclusive Seal in Tee Shirt (#0158) and Polar Bear with Snowflake Scarf (#0159) came with a special stick-on label to distinguish them. The large "E," for exclusive, inside a red circle has never been repeated.

All other World of Coca-Cola exclusive bean bags produced since that time have a second red "Exclusive Everything Coca-Cola" tag.

Many of the bean bags produced for World of Coca-Cola stores and events also have names that indicate their exclusive nature.

The two members-only polar bears produced for the Cavanagh Coca-Cola Christmas Society in 1998 and 1999 can be identified by their names inside the swing tags: "A Collector's Society Exclusive."

Panda bears corresponding with the grand opening of Zoo Atlanta's panda exhibit for the Kroger store chain have both a special second tag and special name "#0322 Coca-Cola exclusive Kroger/Zoo Atlanta Panda Bear." A #0323 World of Coca-Cola edition has a Zoo Atlanta second tag.

NASCAR TAGS

In a total departure from the way Cavanagh had always produced the swing tag on the Coca-Cola brand bean bag plush, the series of NASCAR driver bears all carry special tags.

The front of the round tag has the famous checkerboard contour bottle logo of the Coca-Cola Racing Family of NASCAR drivers. Inside each tag are the driver's number, signature and name on the left side.

NASCA SWING TAG FRONT AND BACK

#88 DALE JARRETT INSIDE TAG

Each NASCAR driver owns the rights to license any product carrying his name, logo and signature. So every tag has to contain specific trademark information about each driver on the right inside of the swing tag.

No doubt this caused a major headache for The Coca-Cola Company to obtain all the trademark permissions before the NASCAR set could be produced. In the end, just eight drivers were represented in the NASCAR bean bag set (instead of an expected twelve). Each swing tag is unique to the driver.

INTERNATIONAL COLLECTION TAGS

By far the most impressive swing tags come on members of the International Bean Bag Collection. The front of the tag is a mul-

OUTSIDE OF HOLOGRAPHIC INTERNATIONAL
SWING TAG SHOWING COLORS

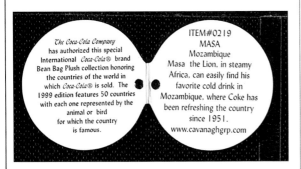

INSIDE OF INTERNATIONAL SWING TAG

2000 CAREER SET SWING TAG FRONT AND BACK, 2000 CAREER SET INSIDE SWING TAG

ticolored hologram globe with a bottle of Coca-Cola. Designed by American Bank Note Holographics, a unique process was used to prevent counterfeiting.

The animal's name (the first time Coca-Cola bean bags were given a specific name) is listed on the left inside of the swing tag, along with the country it represents, a fact about that country and when Coke was first introduced in that country.

Inside the right side of every swing tag is printed: "The Coca-Cola Company has authorized this special International Coca-Cola brand Bean Bag Plush collection honoring the countries of the world in which Coca-Cola is sold. The 1999 edition features 50 countries with each one represented by the animal or bird for which the country is famous."

Since these special holographic swing tags are particularly vulnerable to damage, for the first time they come with custom-designed, bottle-cap-shaped tag protectors installed at the factory before shipping. Unfortunately, the tag protectors are so heavy they fall off easily.

In a complete change from previous bottle-cap swing tags, the 2000 Career set features a new style square tag with the new 2000 fishtail Coca-Cola logo. The new swing tags are in book style printed in both English and French.

The front of the new tag is a brown and beige checkerboard design with the fishtail Coke sign lettering in red. The front states "Coke Bean Bags" in English and French and lists the tag number and name of the bean bag with The Coca-Cola Company website address.

Inside are the copyright notices, in English on the left and in French on the right. On the back is "Distributed by Cavanagh Group International, Alpharetta, Georgia" with CGI's website address.

TAG PROBLEMS

Price stickers on tags: Some retailers appear to be blissfully unaware that placing sticky price tags directly on the swing tag lowers its value to collectors. Over time these price tags wrinkle the swing tag. Several companies now offer a product to remove sticky residue from tags without further damaging them.

Missing tags: Collectors view bean bags without tags as nearly worthless. It is the swing tag that identifies the Coca-Cola brand bean bag plush character and dates it. If you wish to keep your collection valuable, don't remove the tags.

Bent or creased tags: Perfect tags are a collector's goal. While every effort is made to pack and ship bean bags from China with perfect tags, in reality some tags get damaged along the way. Bending, creasing and folding tags lowers the value by half for most collectors.

Marks caused by the plastic strip holding the swing tag are not considered major flaws. Also, curved tags do not lower the value, provided they are not visibly marked. You can rate tag quality by the following criteria:

Mint — tag has no marks, bends, creases, or wear; it lies completely flat and folded on center (MWBT, Mint with both tags).

Near-Mint — tag has tiny marks and/or slight tag curves, especially where it connects to the plastic strip, or it is folded slightly off center (NMWBT near Mint with both tags).

Excellent — tag has minor marks, dings or curves but is not bent, and edges are uneven, or folded off center.

Good — tag is wrinkled but not creased, the shine is off the tag, or it is partially torn from the plastic strip.

Poor — tag is bent, folded, creased, worn and/or damaged.

TAG PROTECTORS

The best way to protect your swing tags is with tag protectors that encase the swing tag with a plastic covering. Cavanagh first installed bottle-cap-shaped tag protectors for the International Bean Bag Collection, but these tag protectors are not available for retail sale apart from this line.

Buyers found the design of these hard plastic tag protectors too heavy and prone to fall off. Redesign of the tag protectors for later sets of International Bean Bags have not helped the problem.

INTERNATIONAL SWING TAG IN TAG PROTECTOR

To date, no manufacturer makes acid-free hard plastic tag protectors specifically for Coca-Cola brand bean bag plush. Tag protectors made for other types of bean bags may work on the Coca-Cola brand. Be sure the tag protector is large enough to protect the valuable waved edges of the tag. Heart-shaped tag protectors can bend the edges and cause the tag to curve.

It is important to stress the need for acid-free tag protectors. All plastic, especially soft varieties, leaks acid. Over time the plastic will bind to the paper tag. When the tag protector is shifted or removed, the printing on the swing tag will adhere to the protector and tear off the tag.

Collectors have lost fortunes because they protected their tags with the wrong kind of plastic.

Most international editions and collector club bean bags (bean bags made especially for The Coca-Cola Collectors Club events) do not have the familiar Coca-Cola bean bag swing tags. This is because these editions are not made by CGI.

The most notable exception is a set of four bean bags made for Kmart stores in Australia in 1998. These bean bags all carried the silver and red bottle-cap swing tag identifying them as Coca-Cola brand bean bag plush. The tag was not a book style but flat with only a front and back.

The 2000 set from Germany features a very different Coca-Cola swing tag (the bottle cap is more three dimensional). None carry style numbers, but all have a special logo made by Play-by-Play.

GERMAN SET SWING TAG AND TUSH TAG

The Australian Football League is releasing sixteen new team polar bears for 2000, each with a distinctive Fan Zone swing tag.

Unnumbered editions are very valuable and often among the most cherished by serious collectors who want every Coca-Cola bean bag plush character made anywhere in

AFL BEAR FAN ZONE SWING TAG

the world. We will discuss these in greater detail in a later chapter.

FAKE TAGS

Protecting its trademarks zealously, The Coca-Cola Company normally grants a license to one company to make each type of merchandise. These licensees pay Coca-Cola a royalty for the use of its trademarks and must go through a rigorous approval process before any item goes into production.

The problem of copyright and trademark infringement is worldwide. Unauthorized sources put the Coca-Cola name on products because they sell. The popularity of bean bag plush has created a growing market for cheap, unauthorized versions.

Where do so-called "third shift" counterfeits come from? Some are rejects that did not meet quality control standards. Others are stolen from plants and resold on the black market, especially in China. Still others are knockoffs, cheap copies made by unlicensed manufacturers.

Since "fake" bean bags often have flaws or inconsistencies, you must educate yourself before you buy. Know what a real swing tag should look like. Ask for photographs. Whenever possible, insist on inspecting the bean bag before purchase. Be sure the quality of the fabric and accessories are consistent with a "real" bean bag.

A recent sale on the Internet proves the point. After a fierce bidding war for Bubbles (the rare Village Cinema polar bear from Australia), the unlucky winner found he had just purchased a much less valuable Burger King Buddy Bear with a pasted on Coke button.

An examination of the photograph accompanying the auction item showed the button was on the wrong side and should have alerted potential buyers.

A sampling of fake tags can be found in Chapter 11.

CHAPTER 3

Mass Market Bean Bags

"Your thirst takes wings"
— 1941 advertising copy

The majority of Coca-Cola brand bean bag plush has been created for the mass market: national and regional chain stores, retail shops, gift and variety outlets.

Originally marketed at Christmas, these happy little critters were soon in demand year-round.

In keeping with the creative marketing philosophy of Coca-Cola, a number of variations have appeared for the mass market. Many bean bags come with shelf hooks for easy display (plastic hooks attached to the head for hanging). Others come packaged singly in plastic bags.

Most come in a bright red display box with a large silver Coca-Cola brand bean bag plush logo on top. Boxes may contain sets of six (the most common) or three depending on the kind of store where they will be sold.

Some may have additional price tags attached to the swing tag. You may find a specific set of bean bags with all of the variations available. All have the same value to collectors.

Retailers may sell bean bags as sets of six or individually, and each decides which line to carry and how many cases to order.

Finding that special bean bag missing from your collection can be quite a challenge. Stores sell out quickly, and few have older editions available.

Now that you are an aficionado of Coca-Cola brand bean bag plush, let's look at all the editions that have been produced to date. We will first list the set by name and year distributed, then the individual bean bags by style number and name, followed by a description.

SPRING 1997 SET (FIRST SET)

Issued 1997/Retired 1997
#0107 Seal in Baseball Cap
#0108 Penguin with
     Delivery Cap
#0109 Polar Bear with
     Bottle
#0110 Polar Bear in
     Pink Bow
#0111 Polar Bear in
     Baseball Cap
#0112 Polar Bear in
     Tee Shirt
Price Guide: $70–90 a set; $15 for individual bean bags.

The phenomenon began when Coca-Cola introduced the first set of six in May of 1997. This first set of six remains one of the most collectible and valuable.

The manufacturer's suggested retail price per piece was $5.99. This set was retired from production in late 1997 but continues to be available on the secondary market. Retail stores specializing in secondary market goods price the set anywhere between $60 and $110. Some Internet auctions may have individual members of this set for $8 to $12 each. It is very hard to find all the members of this set individually.

So-called "first release version" sets are highly prized and valued higher. There are three differences found in the first edition set not seen in later production runs. (Remember, we are not talking about prototypes, but differences between production runs.)

1. #0108 Penguin with Delivery Cap – cap has no button
2. #0109 Polar Bear with Bottle – tag states "Bear with Bottle" (no Polar)
3. #0107 Seal in Baseball Cap – face looks slightly different with oval nose.

Price Guide: $90–120 a set; $20-25 for individual bean bags listed above.

#0111
POLAR BEAR IN
BASEBALL CAP

Mass Market Bean Bags

SPRING 1997 SET

Price Guide: $70-90 a set;
$15 for individual bean
bags.

- **#0107 SEAL IN BASEBALL CAP**

- **#0108 PENGUIN WITH DELIVERY CAP**

- **#0109 POLAR BEAR WITH BOTTLE**

- **#0110 POLAR BEAR IN PINK BOW**

- **#0111 POLAR BEAR IN BASEBALL CAP**

- **#0112 POLAR BEAR IN TEE SHIRT**

WINTER 1997 SET

WINTER 1997 (AKA CHRISTMAS 1997) SET

Issued 1997/Retired 1997

#0101 Seal in Scarf (red striped)

#0102 Seal in Snowflake Cap

#0103 Penguin in Stocking Cap

#0104 Polar Bear in Snowflake Cap

#0105 Polar Bear in Plaid Ribbon

#0106 Polar Bear in Red Bow

Price Guide: $60–90 a set; $15 for individual bean bags.

The second set of Coca-Cola brand bean bag plush released for the Christmas season made an even bigger hit. By early 1998, these cuddly plush toys, dressed in snowflake caps and scarves, had disappeared off store shelves.

The Coca-Cola penguin made his debut with this set. Subtle differences in the faces on the polar bears can be seen in this set:

The faces are smaller and appear to have less stuffing.

As with the Spring 1997 set, various marketing techniques were used. Shelf hooks, individual plastic bag packaging, and boxed sets with only three editions were tested.

New places to sell the bean bags also were tested, including convenience stores, drug stores, markets and even gas stations. Customers began to look for the adorable stuffed animals at their favorite shops and clamored for more.

Retail store prices vary between $50 and $100. Some Internet auctions may have individual members of this set for $8 to $10 each. It is very hard to find all the members of this set individually.

To keep up with the growing demand, Cavanagh created more Coca-Cola bean bag plush characters for 1998, expanding the mass market, adding more exclusives, and creating the Heritage line. (We discuss these in the next chapter.)

SPRING (MASS) 1998 SET

Issued 1998/Retired 1998

#0127 Penguin in Chef's Hat

#0131 Polar Bear in Argyle Shirt

#0135 Walrus with Coca-Cola Bottle

#0136 Husky with Coca-Cola Bottle

#0137 Whale with Coca-Cola Bottle

#0152 Reindeer with Coca-Cola Bottle

Price Guide: $45–60 a set; $9–10 for individual bean bags

Capitalizing on past success, this fourth release of Coca-Cola brand bean bag plush retired ahead of schedule when supplies ran out. Charming new characters included the

#0127 PENGUIN FROM THE SPRING (MASS) 1998 SET

killer whale and husky dog. It is the only time either of these bean bag characters appeared in Coca-Cola sets.

New versions of the ever-popular walrus, penguin and polar bear with exciting new outfits pleased everyone. The #0127 Penguin in Chef's Hat and #0131 Polar Bear in Argyle Shirt remain two of the most desired bean bags.

Retail store prices vary between $42 and $90. Internet auctions often sell individual members of this set for $6 to $10 each. The polar bear and penguin editions from this set are the hardest to find and average $8 to $12.

The next set of Coca-Cola bean bags for the mass market came just in time for holiday shopping.

WINTER (MASS) 1997 SET

Issued 1998/Retired 1998

#0118 Polar Bear in Snowflake Hat

#0120 Polar Bear in Red Scarf

#0123 Seal in Green Scarf

#0141 Walrus in Coca-Cola
     Snowflake Night Cap

#0142 Reindeer in Coca-Cola
     Snowflake Scarf

#0155 Penguin in Coca-Cola Snowflake Scarf

Price Guide: $42–50 a set; $6–8 for individual bean bags

Released in September of 1998, this fifth set turned out to be a hard one for collectors to find. Turning to other sources, collectors created a booming business among the secondary market.

Price Guide: $45-60 a set;
$9-10 for individual bean bags

- **#0127 PENGUIN IN CHEF'S HAT**

- **#0131 POLAR BEAR IN ARGYLE SHIRT**

- **#0135 WALRUS WITH COCA-COLA BOTTLE**

- **#0136 HUSKY WITH COCA-COLA BOTTLE**

- **#0137 WHALE WITH COCA-COLA BOTTLE**

- **#0152 REINDEER WITH COCA-COLA BOTTLE**

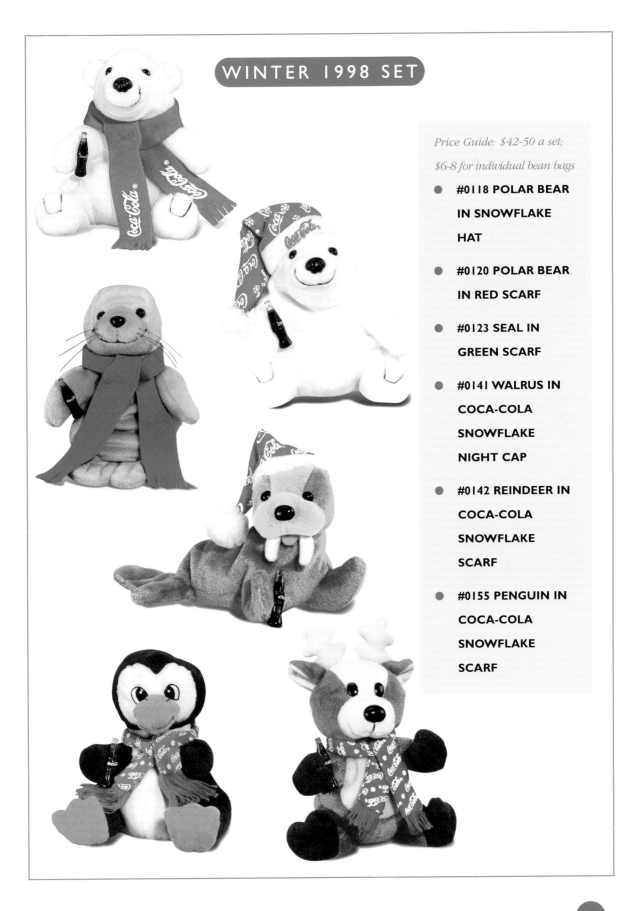

WINTER 1998 SET

Price Guide: $42-50 a set;
$6-8 for individual bean bags

- **#0118 POLAR BEAR IN SNOWFLAKE HAT**

- **#0120 POLAR BEAR IN RED SCARF**

- **#0123 SEAL IN GREEN SCARF**

- **#0141 WALRUS IN COCA-COLA SNOWFLAKE NIGHT CAP**

- **#0142 REINDEER IN COCA-COLA SNOWFLAKE SCARF**

- **#0155 PENGUIN IN COCA-COLA SNOWFLAKE SCARF**

EVERYDAY (MASS) 1999 SET

Checking tags closely became very important with the Winter 1998 set. Many unwary collectors first spied #0118 Polar Bear in Snowflake Hat and thought they'd discovered the rare #0113 Musicland Exclusive Polar Bear in Long Snowflake Cap. Although similar, the size of the bear is smaller and length of stocking cap shorter.

Retail store prices vary between $36 and $60. Individual members of this set retail for $6 to $8. Internet auctions may have them as low as $5 each from time to time. The two polar bears from this set are the hardest to find and average $8 to $10 each.

Snapped up quickly, bean bag enthusiasts were anxious to see what Cavanagh would release the following spring, but delays left them waiting.

EVERYDAY (MASS) 1997 SET

Issued 1999/Retired 1999

#0199 Polar Bear in Plaid Baseball Cap
#0200 Polar Bear in Blue Pattern Shirt
#0201 Polar Bear in Plaid Scarf
#0202 Penguin in Green Pattern Vest
#0203 Seal in Green Pattern Scarf
#0204 Seal in Blue Pattern Baseball Cap
Price Guide: $40–60 a set; $7–8 for individual bean bags

Originally due out in spring, the eighth set released didn't begin shipping to retailers until late fall. Production problems pushed the date back and cut the number of pieces actually available. At one point, Cavanagh stated the set was canceled. Retailers who put in orders early in the year were disappointed when later orders were filled first and supplies ran short.

All members of the Everyday 1999 set feature colorful Coca-Cola trademark fabric. (Any fabric with the Coca-Cola name, red disk icon or contour bottle logo is considered trademark fabric.) Polar bears continue to hold their bottles of Coca-Cola in the left paw while seals and penguins hold their bottles of Coke in their right paws. The popularity of Coca-Cola bean bag characters is attested by the fact that style numbers now ran into the two hundreds.

Retail store prices vary between $40 and $90. Individual members of this set retail for $6 to $8. The three polar bears are the most popular, averaging $8 to $10 each. Because of problems with delivery, many stores that normally carry the Mass line never got this set, pushing up prices.

Because of delays in the Everyday set, some retailers actually got their Winter 1999 set first!

WINTER (MASS) 1999 SET
Issued 1999/Retired 1999

#0205 Penguin in Striped Vest
#0206 Polar Bear in Long Striped Cap
#0207 Seal in Striped Vest & Knit Cap (green)
#0208 Polar Bear in Striped Vest & Bowtie
#0209 Polar Bear in Striped Shirt & Bowtie
#0210 Seal in Striped Scarf & Knit Cap (red)
Price Guide: $36–42 a set; $6–8 for individual bean bags

The Winter 1999 set marked the ninth set released. All the characters are wearing happy winter outfits featuring Coca-Cola trademark fabric with stripes and bubbles in various colors. This set was widely distributed at chain stores, markets, through independent retailers and through catalog sales.

The most popular of the group, Polar Bear in Long Striped Cap, disappeared first and now can be found for $6 to $10. Other individual bean bags retail for $6 to $7. Retail store prices for the set vary between $36 and $60.

ALBERTSON'S WINTER SET 1999

Lucky Winter Set 1999
Sav-On Winter Set 1999
Price Guide: $90–120 a set; $12–15 for individual bean bags

#0210 SEAL IN STRIPED SCARF & KNIT CAP

Price Guide: $36-42 a set;
$6-8 for individual bean bags

- **#0205 PENGUIN IN STRIPED VEST**

- **#0206 POLAR BEAR IN LONG STRIPED CAP**

- **#0207 SEAL IN STRIPED VEST & KNIT CAP (GREEN)**

- **#0208 POLAR BEAR IN STRIPED VEST & BOWTIE**

- **#0209 POLAR BEAR IN STRIPED SHIRT & BOWTIE (NOT SHOWN)**

- **#0210 SEAL IN STRIPED SCARF & KNIT CAP (RED)**

A collector's frenzy developed when three special variations of the Winter 1999 set began appearing at Albertson's supermarkets in various parts of the country. Editions manufactured for this chain of stores carried a special second tag with the market's name.

Albertson's had recently bought out Lucky Markets and Sav-on Drug Stores in parts of the country. Winter bean bags showed up at a few Albertson's with second tags for Lucky or Sav-on.

Since both Lucky and Sav-on were then owned by Albertson's supermarkets and no longer carried their old name, most of the Lucky and Sav-on double tags were removed before shipping. Often both tags were cut off. But many collectors consider the few that were distributed to stores to be errors, thus much more valuable.

It was very hit and miss which stores car-ried the bean bags at all, let alone had the special double tags. For example, in California's Bay Area, just two out of fifty-two Albertson's supermarkets had double-tagged editions available. Ratios were even lower in most other parts of the country.

Another problem developed with the colored display boxes in which the bean bags were shipped. The red dye from the boxes easily rubbed off, permanently stain-ing many bean bags. And the pellet-filled toys lucky enough not to be left in the dis-play boxes were simply dumped into standing metal containers, damaging many tags.

So not only is it hard to find Albertson's, Lucky, and Sav-on second-tagged editions, it is very difficult to find Mint, stain-free ones with good tags.

The few retail stores that carried these special double tags offered individual bean

ALBERTSON'S WINTER SET 1999

YEAR 2000 SET

bags for $6.99 each. Complete sets now retail for $90 to $120 with individual bean bags going at auction for $15 to $25. Very few are available at any price.

Not to miss out on all the Year 2000 excitement, Cavanagh created a special set of four bean bags dressed to party for the event of the century. They began turning up in stores in early fall.

YEAR 2000 SET

Issued 1999/Retired 1999
#0277 Polar Bear in a 2000 Top Hat (boy)
#0278 Polar Bear in a 2000 Vest (girl)
#0279 Seal in a 2000 Vest
#0280 Penguin in a 2000 Scarf
Price Guide: $36–42 a set; $7–8 for individual bean bags

All the members of this 2000 set have a special double tag in red, stating, "Exclusive 2000 design." Each bean bag comes with special 2000 apparel to mark entry into the new year. These playful partygoers quickly moved to the top of just about every Coca-Cola bean bag collector's most-wanted list.

A new marketing venture with a wholesale network company put these adorable 2000 party animals into convenience stores, markets, and other mass-merchandising sources instead of the usual Cavanagh dealers. When Cavanagh saw the astounding attention this special set was getting from the public, the company began marketing to its dealers as well.

Retail store prices vary between $36 and $42 a set. Individual members of this set retail for $6 to $8 with the two bears going for as high as $15 each in Internet auctions. Prices are beginning to creep upward now that the majority of markets and convenience stores are sold out.

#0319
POLAR BEAR IN DELIVERY OUTFIT WITH CAP

EVERYDAY (MASS) 2000

Issued 2000/Retired 2000

#0316 Penguin in Soda Jerk Outfit

#0317 Polar Bear in Soda Jerk Outfit

#0318 Reindeer in Soda Jerk Outfit

#0319 Polar Bear in Delivery Outfit with Cap

#0320 Penguin in Delivery Outfit with Cap

#0321 Seal in Delivery Outfit with Cap

Price Guide: $42–45 a set; $8 for individual bean bags

For the Summer of 2000 a new set of Mass bean bags features old-fashioned delivery outfits and soda jerk costumes.

Dressed for the deep freeze, they are sure to warm collectors' hearts. Greater attention to detail and bright colors gives a new and exciting look to these familiar critters from the North Pole.

Cavanagh promises that many more exciting bean bags will be released in the next few years, with at least two sets per year planned.

#0318
REINDEER IN SODA JERK OUTFIT

- #0319 POLAR BEAR IN DELIVERY OUTFIT WITH CAP

- #0320 PENGUIN IN DELIVERY OUTFIT WITH CAP

- #0321 SEAL IN DELIVERY OUTFIT WITH CAP

- #0317 POLAR BEAR IN SODA JERK OUTFIT

- #0316 PENGUIN IN SODA JERK OUTFIT

- #0318 REINDEER IN SODA JERK OUTFIT

Price Guide: $42-45 a set;
$8 for individual bean bags

CHAPTER 4

Heritage Bean Bags

"Thirst knows no season"
— 1922 slogan

When the Heritage Collection debuted at gift and specialty stores in the spring of 1988, Coca-Cola and Cavanagh knew they had another hit on their hands. Bean bag mania was in full swing, and Coca-Cola brand bean bag plush was climbing the ranks as a collector favorite.

Why create a new line of Coca-Cola bean bags? To fill the need for year-round releases and to make these lovable characters available to a broader group of people than ever before. Cavanagh proudly announced, "Bean Bag Plush are more than just holiday purchases; new additions to the line provide collecting fun all year long."

Heritage bean bags are harder to find because they are produced in fewer numbers than the Mass editions. With only a single production run, sets are automatically retired when store inventories are gone.

Heritage editions are available only at Heritage Collection retailers: gift stores, specialty shops, Christmas stores and boutiques. To find a Heritage Collection retailer in your area check out the Cavanagh Website (www.cavanaghgrp.com) or the Coca-Cola Christmas Society annual Product and Retail Guide. If none are available, Cavanagh can give you a list of retailers who ship outside their area.

Some Heritage Collection retailers carry both the Heritage and the Mass line of bean bags. Each determines what products to carry and may not have every edition available. The suggested retail price for Heritage bean bags is $6 each, but each individual dealer determines the actual selling price.

1998 SPRING (HERITAGE)
#0124 WALRUS
WITH ACCESSORY BENCH

SPRING (HERITAGE) EVERYDAY SET 1998

Issued 1998/Retired 1998

#0114 Seal in Ski Cap

#0116 Polar Bear in Sweater

#0124 Walrus with Coca-Cola Bottle
and Logo Scarf

#0132 Coca-Cola Can in Shades

#0133 Reindeer in Shirt

SPRING
(HERITAGE)
EVERYDAY SET 1998

#0140 Polar Bear in Drivers Cap and Bowtie
Price Guide: $60–80 a set; $10–15 for individual bean bags

Considered the third release of bean bags, the first Heritage set began popping up in stores across the country in May, 1998. The same set was released in Canada.

Four new bean bag plush characters made their first appearance: the reindeer, husky, walrus and can of Coke with sunglasses. Everyone loved these whimsical new toys. But the favorites continued to be the original cuddly polar bear and seal.

Retail store prices vary widely on this set from $42 to $120. Individual members of this set retail for $10 to $18. Internet auctions continue to offer individual members for $6 to $8, but complete sets are rare and prices can be volatile. On the same day recently, two Internet auctions for the Coca-Cola can with shades closed at $4.80 and $22.50.

Also introduced for the first time with the Heritage collection were five playful accessories. A director's chair, sling chair, bench, Coca-Cola crate and wooden six pack made for a fun way to display bean bag characters.

With growing importance placed on swing tags and tag numbers, this was the first set not to have sequential numbers. Collectors wondered if new bean bags would fill the missing tag numbers soon.

They only had to wait until September for the next Her-

itage set to arrive in gift and specialty stores across the nation.

WINTER HERITAGE (GIFT) SET 1998
Issued 1998/Retired 1999
#0167 Polar Bear in Checker Cap & Scarf
#0168 Reindeer with a Colorful Coca-Cola
      Vest & Hat
#0169 Polar Bear in Blue Night Cap
#0170 Seal in Delivery Outfit (blue)
#0171 Polar Bear in Soda Fountain Outfit (red)
#0172 Penguin in Holiday Vest
Price Guide: $42–60 a set; $8–10 for individual bean bags

All of the bean bags in this released set (No. 6) sported very detailed outfits with Coca-Cola trademark fabric. From the Soda Fountain Polar Bear to the Delivery Seal, each of the lovable designs immediately tugged at shoppers' heartstrings, and these toys flew out of stores across America and Canada. Once again consecutively numbered, collectors found it easy to keep track of the new editions.

A completely redesigned and larger Reindeer (#0168) de-buted with this set. Larger and much more detailed

1998 WINTER
HERITAGE
#0172 PENGUIN
WITH ACCESSORY SLEIGH

WINTER HERITAGE SET 1998

than previous editions, the reindeer with an irresistible smile now had a bigger nose, different fabric, larger antlers and stitched feet, giving it a more playful appeal.

Many gift retailers continue to have this set available for $36 to $60. Individual members of this set can be found for $8 to $10 in stores and $6 to $8 on Internet auction sites. The most popular Polar Bear in Soda Fountain Outfit is the hardest to find individually.

Three accessories also came new with the set: a sleigh, wagon and truck, helping to make home displays of collections more fun and exciting.

Always looking for new ways to market the Coca-Cola bean bags, Cavanagh joined forces with two cooperative buying groups of gift retailers in 1998. Gift Creation Concepts (GCC) and Parade of Gift Retailers (POG) both offer independent retailers across the country a cost-effective tool to reach more customers.

These groups buy exclusive and specialty items in large quantities, then produce a catalog of products twice a year. Member retailers receive the same catalog, but each one is customized with their name and contact information to mail to customers.

Part of the Heritage Collection, two exclusive Coca-Cola polar bears were distributed by these retail groups in their 1998 Christmas catalogs. Only five thousand of each bean bag, and twenty-five hundred of the exclusive accessories, were made. Collectors went wild trying to locate a member store in their area. Many stores limited customers to two of these adorable stuffed toys.

POG EXCLUSIVE 1998

Issued 1998/Retired 1998
#0165 Polar Bear in Blue/Green
Checkered Vest
Price Guide: $25–45 each; $25–40 for the matching sling chair

This exclusive polar bear came with the first exclusive accessory: a matching fabric sling chair. Both bean bag and chair were only available at Parade of Gift Retailers advertised through their catalog for $42 (polar bear with chair).

GCC EXCLUSIVE 1998

Issued 1998/Retired 1998
#0166 Polar Bear in
Blue Striped
Delivery Suit
Price Guide: $25-45 each; $30-40 for the matching two-pack box

The swing tag states "A GCC Exclusive." This happy bear came with an exclusive two-pack red wooden box. Some retailers sold the bear and box as a pair for $45; others

sold the polar bear and box separately for $15. With two red Coke buttons, a blue-striped delivery outfit and bowtie, this little guy remains one of the all-time favorites.

Even more excitement, and plenty of controversy, followed in 1999 regarding the Heritage line of Coca-Cola bean bags. Coca-Cola announced a major change in the way polar bears looked on a QVC television segment. The literature read on the air stated:

#0165 POLAR BEAR
WITH CHAIR FROM
PARADE OF GIFTS
CATALOG

GCC EXCLUSIVE 1998 #0166 POLAR BEAR

"The new design portrays the more authentic look of the advertising characters, while still retaining the whimsy, fun and charm the plush bears have come to represent."

"New face" polar bears debuted with the spring release of the new GCC Exclusive for the Heritage line.

GCC EXCLUSIVE 1999
Issued 1999/Retired 1999
#0267 Polar Bear in Red Romper
Price Guide: $25–30 each

Totally redesigned, the new face bears now had a different body shape, smaller face, new eyes with eyelids, a narrower and flatter nose and stitched hands and feet with patches of gray fabric to make them look more like paws. Even the famous Coca-Cola bottle was shifted to the opposite left hand, on the underside of the paw.

Collectors either loved the new design or hated it. And retailers heard about it from angry customers who wanted the familiar happy face back. But the Coca-Cola decision to make the polar bear look more like the advertisements stood firm. All future polar bears had the new face design, and the hunt was on for collectors to gather up all the old face editions they could find.

Fortunately, Coca-Cola bean bag collectors were so in love with the characters, even such a momentous change in design did not slow the buying frenzy. They liked the shiny

GCC EXCLUSIVE 1999
#0267 POLAR BEAR IN RED ROMPER

fabric of the Coca-Cola red romper with green trim even though most couldn't figure out what a romper was supposed to look like.

It is extremely difficult to find this exclusive bear at retail stores. Internet auctions only occasionally feature one, usually for $20 to $35.

The Sporting set debuted in May with all new face bears and familiar seal and penguin characters.

SPORTING SET 1999

Issued 1999/Retired 1999

#0261 Polar Bear in Baseball Jersey

#0262 Polar Bear in Football Jersey

#0263 Penguin in Hockey Shirt

#0264 Polar Bear in Red Golf Shirt

#0265 Polar Bear in Ski Outfit

#0266 Seal in Soccer Shirt

Price Guide: $36–48 a set; $8 for individual bean bags

SPORTING SET 1999
#0265 POLAR BEAR (PROTOTYPE "OLD FACE")

Unlike any set issued previously, this set had finely detailed clothing and accessories all on one theme: sports! Enthusiasts grabbed up the ones that represented their favorite activity. A California newscast showed a kid's soccer team with members all holding their favorite seal in a soccer shirt.

New retailers clamored to enter the Heritage Collection with the introduction of this set. Unlike the familiar polar characters depicted in various winter outfits, this set reflected the growing interest in sports bean bags, especially sports bears. Detailed jerseys, caps and shirts put Coca-Cola brand bean bags in a league with the other heavy hitters competing for the exceptional bean bag plush market.

So what did CGI do for an encore? The newest members of the Heritage Collection made their first appearance at trade shows for Gift

CAREER SET
2000 #0314
PENGUIN
PILOT

Accessories

SPRING
HERITAGE
(EVERYDAY)
SET 1998

WINTER
HERITAGE
(GIFT) SET 1998

Sporting Set 1999

(PROTOTYPE "OLD FACE" BEAN BAGS)

Price Guide: $36-48 a set;

$8 for individual bean bags

- **#0261 POLAR BEAR IN BASEBALL JERSEY**

- **#0262 POLAR BEAR IN FOOTBALL JERSEY**

- **#0263 PENGUIN IN HOCKEY SHIRT**

- **#0264 POLAR BEAR IN RED GOLF SHIRT**

- **#0265 POLAR BEAR IN SKI OUTFIT**

- **#0266 SEAL IN SOCCER SHIRT**

Retailers in early 2000. Sellers were not disappointed.

CAREER SET 2000

Issued 2000/Retired 2000

#0310 Polar Bear Fireman (boots,
　　　suspenders & hat)

#0311 Polar Bear Construction Worker
　　　(overalls & cap)

#0312 Reindeer Artist (jacket & beret)

#0313 Seal Chef (apron & chef's hat)

#0314 Penguin Pilot (scarf, aviator cap &
　　　goggles)

#0315 Polar Bear Policeman (jacket & hat)

*Price Guide: $45 a set; $8 for individual
bean bags*

#0310 POLAR BEAR
FIREMAN

Each adorable bean bag in the Career set represents a specific occupation easily identified by its outfit. Fine detailing has gone into this production from the policeman's jacket buttons to the fireman's boots to the artist's jaunty beret.

The most unusual feature of these bean bags is their new style of swing tag. No longer bottle-cap shaped, these square, book-style swing tags feature the new 2000 Coca-Cola logo. Printed in brown and beige, the tag features a checkerboard design on the old-style fishtail sign with Coke in red lettering.

The Career set is available at gift retailers and through catalog sales. Pre-sales of this set drew new Coca-Cola bean bag enthusiasts, eager to get into collecting, to stores and websites.

Career Set 2000

CHAPTER 5

Exclusive Bean Bags

*"I've been thirsty,
and I've been refreshed,
and believe me, refreshed is better"
— 1969 advertising copy*

Some Coca-Cola bean bag plush are produced exclusively for specific companies. They are used in special promotions — particularly to sell Coca-Cola products — for special events, and occasions such as store anniversaries.

The term "exclusive" is used for the bean bags that are available only from a single company or group of stores. Exclusive bean bags are the most desired and hardest to find.

Along with the successful first two sets of Coca-Cola bean bag plush characters in 1997, Cavanagh produced exclusive bean bags for three different companies.

Issued 1997/Retired 1997
#0113 Polar Bear in Long
Snowflake Cap
Price Guide: $400-600

Available only during the
Christmas season in 1997, this
polar bear remains scarce. The
Musicland polar bear is taller and fatter than
other Coca-Cola polar bears, standing eight
inches high with the longest snowflake cap
yet designed.

Only five thousand were sold at Musicland and Media Play stores in the Midwest
and on the East Coast. Some stores required
customers to make a $25 purchase before
they could buy this lovable polar bear

for $5.99. Others gave it
away with a $100 purchase.
Sales shot through the roof.

Collectors cringe thinking
how many of these rare
bears ended up as children's
toys. Rarely do you see one
for sale on the secondary
market, and when you do,
it fetches anything from $275
to $800 in Mint condition. About every three
to four months, one appears for sale on Internet auction sites.

It is estimated only one thousand of
these polar bears exist in Mint condition today.
Every once in a while a rumor circulates
about someone walking into a Musicland
store and finding one of these rare
polar bears waiting to be discovered.

BLOCKBUSTER
EXCLUSIVE
CHRISTMAS
1997

Issued 1997/Retired 1997

#0144 Polar Bear with
Green Bow

#0145 Seal with Green
Scarf

#0146 Polar Bear in
Driver's Cap

#0147 Seal in Long
Stocking Cap

#0148 Penguin in
Snowflake Cap

#0149 Polar Bear in Red
Vest and Black
Bowtie

Price Guide: $240–360 a set; $35–50 each

Another exclusive Christmastime Coca-Cola bean bag plush promotion came from Blockbuster stores. This set of six bean bag characters featured the most detailed outfits to date.

As advertised in a store catalog, the purchase of a $25 or $50 gift certificate was required to get one of these exclusive toys. Not every store received all six editions, so collectors were challenged to acquire this elusive set.

This set has unique tags with the added price tab. Although the tabs state that each bean bag sells for $5.99, very few stores actually sold the toys individually. The stores quickly realized what a terrific marketing tool bean bags could be.

BLOCKBUSTER CATALOG

This extra tab made the swing tags more vulnerable to tearing, bending and folding, and it is very difficult to find complete sets with Mint tags. Extra care has to be taken to preserve these tags because they fit no tag protector made.

Retail stores rarely carry this entire set, and prices vary widely from $180 to $400. For a while, Internet auctions featured individual Blockbuster bean bags regularly for $20 to $25. This set has become harder to find as collectors seek these early editions and are willing to pay to find a complete set.

The Polar Bear with Green Bow, Penguin in Snowflake Cap, and Polar Bear in Red Vest and Black Bowtie are the hardest to find and sell for $5 to $8 more per bean bag.

Issued 1997/Retired 1997

#0153 Polar Bear in Green Ribbon (girl)

#0154 Polar Bear in Striped Scarf (boy)

Price Guide: $60–65 a pair

This exclusive pair was produced for the respected *White's Guide to Collecting Figures.*

WHITE'S GUIDE
EXCLUSIVE KISSING BEARS 1997

The Coca-Cola Kissing Bears were limited to fifteen thousand sets, sold though the magazine and later on the *White's Guide* website.

Once *White's Guide to Collecting Figures* began listing Coca-Cola brand bean bag plush in its value guide, collecting became serious business.

These lovable polar bears literally attract one another with magnets in their noses. Unfortunately the magnets used for these popular bears were weak to begin with and demagnetized over time. Occasionally the magnets are reversed in the pairs and they actually repel each other!

A trick to keep them kissing is to place a stronger magnet (be sure it is clean) between their noses, and always store the bears apart from each other. Scanners used in post offices, at airports, and even grocery stores can also demagnetize them.

By summer of 1998, *White's Guide* reported it had sold out of these lovable Kissing Bears. Quickly, a secondary market developed for this popular pair and prices began to rise. What originally sold for $15.95 soon fetched $50 to $60 a pair.

Unfortunately, in late 1999 *White's Guide* went into bankruptcy and the publisher's stock was liquidated. Cases of "non-kissing" Kissing Bears with weak magnets were dumped onto the wholesale market. These "non-kissing" bears began appearing in grocery stores, convenience stores and other outlets for low prices — a disaster for serious collectors. Fortunately, the market for "kissing" Kissing Bears continues to be strong.

The first three exclusive Coca-Cola brand bean bags proved the marketing potential of these cuddly critters. Teaming them up with store promotions, Coca-Cola could sell more soft drinks, more videos, more merchandise, even more meals in restaurants. The exclusive market opened a whole new world for Coca-Cola bean bag lovers.

In 1998 two companies who had already seen their sales skyrocket entered into exclusive agreements with Cavanagh for a second edition of their successful bean bags.

2ND EDITION WHITE'S GUIDE
EXCLUSIVE KISSING BEARS 1998
Issued 1998/Retired 1999
#0182 Polar Bear in Blue Bowtie & Vest (boy)
#0183 Polar Bear in Red Bow & Jumper (girl)
Price Guide: $25 a pair

2ND EDITION WHITE'S GUIDE EXCLUSIVE
KISSING BEARS 1998

The second pair of Kissing Bears produced exclusively for *White's Guide to Collecting Figures* appeared in mid-1998. This time the pair had strong magnets that kept them kissing. A limited run of fifteen thousand pairs were made and distributed only through *White's Guide* magazine, its website and special events. Since they were never available through stores, collectors turned to the secondary market to find these special editions.

The bears come sealed in a plastic bag for protection. They are dressed in blue-and-white-striped vests and dresses featuring the Coca-Cola trademark, with red hair bows for the "girl" and blue bowties for the "boy."

Since only *White's Guide to Collecting Figures* carried this second edition of Kissing Bears, prices began rising once stock was depleted. Secondary market prices are very uniform at $20–25 a pair.

The Musicland chain of stores (now Media Play and Suncoast Motion Picture Stores) also saw a tremendous demand for a second exclusive edition. Just in time for the holiday rush, three new designs appeared in stores across the country.

MEDIA PLAY EXCLUSIVE 1998

Issued 1998/Retired 1998

#0161 Polar Bear in Cream & Green
    Checkered Shirt
#0162 Reindeer with a Coca- Cola Holiday
    Shirt
#0163 Polar Bear in Holiday Scarf
#1064 Seal in a Holiday Cap
Price Guide: $60–75 a set, $15–25 each

What immediately catches your eye with this set of four is the second bright orange "Exclusive to Us" tag. Larger than the regular Cavanagh silver swing tag, this marker easily identifies the exclusive set of two old face polar bears, new design reindeer and familiar seal.

Three of the characters are wearing Coca-Cola identified dark green fabric outfits with bottles of Coke, stockings and holly decorating the fabric. The last polar bear has green-and-white-checked fabric on its vest similar to the blue-and-green-checked fabric used with the POG Polar Bear #0165.

Sold individually, not all stores received equal amounts of all four happy little characters, leaving collectors scrambling to complete a set.

Some stores placed price tags on the swing tags, or anti-theft tags directly on the bean bag characters that left a sticky residue when removed. Sometimes the swing tags actually tore when the price tags were removed. The bright orange tag also reportedly fades if not protected from direct light, which has added to the difficulty of getting perfect tags.

Secondary prices for this exclusive set continue to rise as members become harder and harder to find. The Polar Bear in Holiday Scarf seems to be the hardest member of this group to locate. Internet auctions occasionally offer complete sets as well as individual bean bags. One recent auction brought $120 for the set of four.

Exclusive editions were proving to be a real challenge for die-hard collectors determined to own every single one produced. By far the most collectible (and most expensive) Coca-Cola bean bag comes from a different kind of exclusive promotion: a free gift to a targeted group.

McDONALD'S OWNERS CONVENTION 1998
Issued 1998/Retired 1998
Boy and Girl Polar Bears (without numbers)
Price Guide: $500–800 a pair

A very special exclusive pair was given to attendees at the annual McDonald's Owner's/Operator's Convention held in Orlando, Florida, in 1998. Reports on how many were actually produced and distributed vary from five thousand to twenty-two thousand. What is clear is that attendees snapped them up and kept them for themselves. Only rarely do these bears appear on the secondary market, and when they do, they command a hefty sum.

The "boy" polar bear is wearing a red vest that states, "1998 Worldwide Convention,

MEDIA PLAY EXCLUSIVE 1998 SET

McDONALD'S OWNERS CONVENTION 1998
BOY AND GIRL POLAR BEARS

for the pair shows prices ranging from a steal at $275 to an amazing $982. One Japanese buyer paid $1,200 for a pair to complete his collection! Yet every once in a while, the boy bear shows up at swap meets for less than $100, so keep your eyes open.

Orlando," along with McDonald's "Golden Arches" logo. The "girl" polar bear has a red bow, but she actually was supposed to have a matching dress with McDonald's logo.

When the two bears where shipped to Coca-Cola before the convention, neither had their outfits attached. The boy bear's vest fit nicely over his head without a problem, but the girl bear's dress proved to be too small. It could not be jammed, shoved, pushed or pulled over her head, and dozens of girl bears reportedly lost their noggins in the attempt. With the convention date fast approaching, the dresses were discarded and the polar bears were paired up for distribution.

Determining a price for this rare pair is difficult since fewer than fifty pairs are bought and sold each year. Just four to five pairs show up for auction on the Internet each year and only a handful of secondary market stores have them available from time to time.

A sampling of past Internet auction prices

Some sources indicate McDonald's Owner/Operator's Convention polar bears have tag numbers #0156-0157. These tag numbers were originally reserved for the McDonald's pair, but tags were never attached to the bears and remain unused.

THANKS A BILLION BEAR 1998
Issued 1998/Retired 1998
Unknown Polar Bear
Price Guide: value unknown

Not much is known about the "Thanks a Billion" bear, given to Coca-Cola stockholders at an April 1998 annual meeting. Supposedly to celebrate the one billionth drink of Coke, it shows up on lists of Coca-Cola bean bag plush and in posts on the Internet. Cavanagh representatives report that the bear exists but are unable to provide any other details, and no one I have spoken to has found one. Supposedly a Cavanagh product without a tag number, the bear remains a bit of a mystery.

Another type of food promotion introduced the first Chinese Coca-Cola polar bear in November of 1998.

MANCHU WOK BEAR 1998
Issued 1998/Retired 1998
#0177 Polar Bear Dressed in Red Satin Jacket
(American & Canadian Versions)
Price Guide: $12–15 American version;
$15–20 Canadian version

What a unique idea. Use the famous Coca-Cola Polar Bear bean bag dressed in a Chinese outfit to sell Coca-Cola products and Chinese food.

In conjunction with Coca-Cola the Manchu Wok restaurant chain, based in Canada and located in twenty-five states, came up with a great marketing plan: In order to purchase this exclusive Chinese

bear, you had to buy any combo meal and a large Coca-Cola. For each meal purchased, you could buy a bear for the suggested price of $2.99.

People flocked to these Chinese fast-food restaurants located in malls, airports, and shopping centers just to get the newest Coca-Cola bean bag. Stories of collectors purchasing ten servings of fried rice just to buy the bears were not uncommon. If there wasn't a restaurant in their area, some collectors begged friends living near a Manchu Wok to go and have a Chinese lunch on them just to get the little bear.

Dozens of these adorable little bears flooded the secondary market when Manchu Wok restaurants dropped the food purchase requirement at the end of the promotion. They still frequently show up on Internet auction sites for $10 to $15 apiece.

These darling little Chinese bears have a special white, rectangular Manchu Wok tag and come in sealed plastic bags. Both the bears with single English tags and double English/French tags from Canada are highly collectible. Most enthusiasts want both.

More special, exclusive bean bags from Coca-Cola followed in 1999 to the delight of bean bag collectors everywhere. All the polar bears have new faces, great new outfits, and bring lots of fun.

#0177 POLAR
BEAR DRESSED
IN RED SATIN
JACKET

MEDIA PLAY/MUSICLAND EXCLUSIVE 1999

MEDIA PLAY/MUSICLAND EXCLUSIVE 1999

Issued 1999/Retired 1999

#0287 Polar Bear in Red Soda Jerk Vest

#0288 Polar Bear in Suspenders

#0289 Polar Bear in Red Delivery Jacket

Price Guide: $45-60 a set, $12-15 each

These three polar bears, arguably the cutest threesome you'll ever see, arrived at Musicland and Suncoast stores just before Christmas. With red suspenders, a soda jerk hat, and red delivery outfit — not to mention that great smile — collectors fell in love. All have the second, larger "Exclusive to Us" tag in black and gold.

Different stores tried different promotions to peddle these annual favorites. Some required a minimum purchase of $25, while others allowed direct sale.

The first to disappear off the shelves was the Polar Bear in Red Suspenders with his flour sack fabric cap and brown pants, complete with a hole for his tail. Getting all three was a challenge in some locations, but an emphasis on advertising brought in a whole new crowd to enjoy these wonderful bean bag friends.

The supply of these special three bears is gone in most MediaPlay stores, so the main source is the secondary market. Prices already have risen from $10 each in December 1999 to $15-20.

McDONALD'S OPERATIONS
BOSTON REGION POLAR BEAR 1999

Issued 1999/Retired 1999

Price Guide: Estimate $600–1000

The rarest of the rare Coca-Cola bean bags was given to upper management in McDonald's Operations Group in the Boston

Region in 1999. Very little information is available on this special exclusive bear because it has only appeared for sale once or twice on the Internet. Most collectors have no idea this special bear exists!

This cuddly little old face bear comes dressed a white tee with yellow sleeves. The red wording on the shirt states, "McDonald's Operations Boston Region 1999." There is nothing on the back. This bear comes with no swing tag and a standard Cavanagh tush tag, dated 1998.

The story behind this special Polar Bear is this: After the McDonald's Owners Convention was over in 1998, several bean bags had not been used (because of the problem with the girl bear's dress not fitting over her head). Coca-Cola bought the bears made by CGI and used a few for special promotions with McDonald's management.

McDONALD'S OPERATIONS BOSTON REGION POLAR BEAR 1999

The polar bear without special clothing or tags was adapted for this event by adding a white and yellow tee shirt. Will we see more limited distribution of the same polar bears with different clothing?

More "blank" bears exist than have yet been seen, so it is very possible.

Tracking this rare bear down is the ultimate challenge for collectors who want every bean bag Coca-Cola has ever made. Only a very limited number were given to the upper management team from the Boston Operations area of McDonalds. The price guide is an estimate based on such limited sales, but it could go up when collectors discover this special bear.

CARROWS RESTAURANT
POLAR BEAR PAIR 1999

Issued 1999/Retired 2000
#186 Polar Bear in Red Tank Top
#187 Polar Bear in Red Striped Scarf
Price Guide: $25–30 each

Sneaking into the Coca-Cola brand bean bag plush lineup just in time for Christmas was an exclusive pair of old face bears designed for the Carrows Restaurant chain in California.

Not appearing on any list, no one expected them. Most collectors found them by mistake.

Restaurants placed a sign over the cash register with the two dis-

CARROWS
RESTAURANT POLAR
BEAR PAIR 1999

played. They required a Coca-Cola product purchase with your meal before you could buy one of the bears.

They're smaller than any previously made Coca-Cola bean bag bears but still larger than the "Mini Collectible" size. Collectors were confused by the style numbers, as bean bags produced with such low numbers were long retired.

By New Year's most restaurants were sold out of the surprising little bears that had boosted Coca-Cola sales all holiday season. Only a handful of secondary market retailers offer this rare pair. Internet auctions featured just a few individual bears at Christmastime with none available into the New Year. Prices can only go up for this darling little pair of bears.

What lies ahead for exclusive Coca-Cola bean bag plush? Look for new editions to come out at the holiday season again. Since there is no organized way to know when

and where exclusive bean bags might be arriving in your area, here are some tips:

- Check websites that list Coca-Cola bean bags to see what's new. One list of all Coca-Cola bean bags available is updated weekly:
  www.4beanies-cola.com/beanbaglist.html
- Look for new listings on Internet auction sites.
- Ask your Cavanagh retailer to let you know when new editions are released. If they don't regularly carry an item, ask them to special order it for you.
- Members of the Cavanagh Coca-Cola Collectors Society can get information about upcoming editions from quarterly newsletters.
- Ask retailers who have sold exclusive editions in the past if they are getting new exclusives in the future (MediaPlay, Blockbuster, etc.).

CHAPTER 6

World of Coca-Cola Exclusives

"Coke – after Coke – after Coke"
— 1966 advertising copy

WORLD OF COCA-COLA, ATLANTA

The ultimate destination for any Coca-Cola enthusiast is the World of Coca-Cola in Atlanta, Georgia. The three-story building (forty-five thousand square feet) features a collection of thousands of original artifacts, memorabilia, rare packaging and historical documents.

You can drink Coca-Cola dispensed by a twenty-foot fountain that plays famous jingles. Or you can try one of the many flavors of soft drinks sold by Coca-Cola throughout the world.

Watch advertisements on large screens that tell the history of the company. Explore the museum displaying John Pemberton's original equipment. Step up to an old-fashioned soda fountain.

But don't miss the Everything Coca-Cola store featuring many varieties of the Company's available product. It is home to some of the most collectible exclusive bean bags made by Cavanagh.

The Everything Coca-Cola stores featuring exclusive bean bags are located at the World of Coca-Cola in Atlanta, on the "Strip" in Las Vegas, and the specialty store at the Atlanta Hartsfield Airport. A new store also opened in Tokyo in the spring of 2000. (Addresses are listed in Appendix B.)

Everything Coca-Cola stores also carry selected Heritage Collection bean bags, but may not have complete sets available at any given time.

COCA-COLA EXCLUSIVE PAIR 1998

Issued 1998/
Retired 1998
Reissued 1998/Retired 1999
(bear only)
#0158 Seal in Tee Shirt
#0159 Polar Bear in Red
Coca-Cola
Snowflake Scarf
(old/new face)
Price Guide: $75–100
seal; $25–30 old face "E"

#0158 SEAL IN TEE SHIRT FROM COCA-COLA EXCLUSIVE PAIR 1998

tag bear; $20–25 old face double tag bear; $7–15 new face double tag bear

The first bean bags produced exclusively for World of Coca-Cola and available only at the Everything Coca-Cola stores, included an adorable seal sporting a white tee and a polar bear with a long red scarf.

Both had an unusual swing tag issued only for the first production run. A large stick-on label with an "E," for exclusive, in a red circle was added to the front of the regular Cavanagh bottle cap swing tag after production. This swing tag has never been issued again.

Only one production run was ever done on the seal, which disappeared quickly. Prices have skyrocketed with rising demand for this special exclusive seal as sources have

become very few and far between. What once sold for $8, now retails for $75, $100, even $200.

The Polar Bear in Red Coca-Cola Snowflake Scarf, on the other hand, has been reissued several times in three different versions:

1. Old face polar bear with E exclusive swing tag — first production run only, 1998. This remains the most collectible because it was available for such a short time with the special tag. Prices range from $20 to $25 each.

2. Old face polar bear with red exclusive Everything Coca-Cola double tag — second production run, late 1998. Retired in 1999, the prices of this second run have risen in the past year to $20 to $25 each. Few sources have double-tagged editions available.

THREE VERSIONS OF #159 POLAR BEAR

3. New face polar bear with red exclusive Everything Coca-Cola double tag — third production quickly replaced the reissued second run in June of 1999. This edition has a different scarf made of heavier material. Available off and on at the Everything Coca-Cola stores,

WORLD OF COCA-COLA STORE EXCLUSIVES 1998/1999

collectors still turn to the secondary market for this happy little bear with a new face.

Collectors view all three versions as different, highly collectible bean bags. The first two have totally disappeared from Everything Coca-Cola stores, but the third is available until current supplies run out. It is unclear if a fourth production run will be made for this bear.

WORLD OF COCA-COLA STORE EXCLUSIVES
1998/1999

Issued 1998/Retired 1998/Reissued 1999
#0191 Polar Bear in World of Coca-Cola
    Atlanta Tee Shirt
#0192 Polar Bear in World of Coca-Cola
    Las Vegas Tee Shirt
Price Guide: $20–25 each old face, $7–15 each new face; Las Vegas polar bear should increase $5–10 each in 2000

This lovable pair of bears were only available at the World of Coca-Cola stores in Atlanta and Las Vegas. Dressed in red tee shirts, they proudly bear the yellow logo of World of Coca-Cola with the city name at the bottom. Both come with double exclusive Everything Coca-Cola tags.

Actually the World of Coca-Cola Las Vegas polar bears first arrived with no second exclusive tag. All had to be retagged at the store. Some of the polar bears had their Cavanagh swing tags cut off and both tags reattached, while others got a second (and much longer) plastic strip to attach the second tag. A few got out with only single tags and are considered "mistakes."

Like the #0159 Polar Bear in Red Coca-Cola Snowflake Scarf, several production runs have resulted in differences (although numbers have not changed):

1. Old face polar bears with double exclusive Everything Coca-Cola tags — 1998. Prices vary from $20-25 each on the secondary market. Atlanta and Las Vegas stores sold out of this old face edition in 1999.

2. New face polar bears with double exclusive Everything Coca-Cola tags — 1999. Both stores currently carry this version until supplies run out.

With the closure of the World of Coca-Cola museum in Las Vegas in March of 2000, the #0192 Polar Bear with the World of Coca-Cola museum logo will become much more valuable. Future reissues of this bear will have the Everything Coca-Cola logo (red) instead of the World of Coca-Cola logo (yellow).

Problems occur with the yellow World of Coca-Cola logo on the T-shirt. If it gets bent or folded in any way, the rubberized insignia can crack, peel and flake off. Earlier editions have more problems than later ones. It is important to store these exclusive bean bags carefully.

1st ANNUAL COKE COLLECTORS CLASSIC EXCLUSIVE 1998

Issued 1998/Retired 1998
#0184 Polar Bear in Collector Classic
       Tee Shirt
Price Guide: $25–40 each

On October 24, 1998, a special event took place at World of Coca-Cola Atlanta. The first annual Collectors Classic featured an exclusive polar bear bean bag and matching Coke bottle. Just eighteen hundred of the special bean bags were made, and they sold out in a matter of hours. Special events, displays and entertainment helped draw large crowds to the soon-to-be annual event.

Everyone waited for the other two Everything Coca-Cola stores in New York and at the Atlanta Hartsfield Airport to get their own exclusive polar bear. Because of production problems,

WOC ATLANTA EXCLUSIVES OLD AND NEW FACE

1st ANNUAL COKE COLLECTORS
CLASSIC EXCLUSIVE 1998

COCA-COLA FORMAL PAIR 1998
Issued 1998/Retired –

#0193   Polar Bear in Black Velvet Vest (boy)

#0194   Polar Bear in Red Satin Collar
       & Bow (girl)

Price Guide: $40–50 a pair

Called the "Formal Pair," the boy bear comes dressed in a black satin jacket with red trim. The girl comes in a matching black collar and red satin bow. Both are sewn together at the wrists and come in a sealed plastic bag.

Formal pair bears were a smashing hit with collectors and the general public. They appeared on wedding cakes and were given away as birthday and anniversary gifts.

They are currently still available in small numbers at all the Everything Coca-Cola stores. When the supply is gone, it is unclear

the Everything Coca-Cola store on 5th Avenue changing locations, and delays in other sets, no old face polar bears were issued for the other two stores.

Production problems also plagued other exclusives made just for World of Coca-Cola stores in 1998. An exclusive set of six to be released only at the Atlanta store for Christmas got so delayed that only two bean bags out of the set were released late in the year.

COCA-COLA FORMAL PAIR 1998

WORLD OF COCA-COLA EXCLUSIVE STORE SET 1999

if they will be reissued in new face editions. Secondary market prices have varied widely with Formal Pairs, selling for as much as $75 around Valentine's Day and June weddings.

WORLD OF COCA-COLA EXCLUSIVE STORE SET 1999

Issued 1999/Retired –

#0191   Polar Bear in World of Coca-Cola Atlanta Tee Shirt

#0192   Polar Bear in World of Coca-Cola Las Vegas Tee Shirt

#0270   Polar Bear in Everything Atlanta Tee Shirt

#0271   Polar Bear in Everything New York Tee Shirt

Price Guide: $8–15 each

In 1999 new face editions for all four locations finally became available. The first two reissues of previous #0191 and #0192

bears did not change numbers or names. The second two now were named "Everything" for the Everything Coca-Cola stores they represented. Each bear can only be purchased at its respective store.

Eight exciting new exclusive editions arrived at World of Coca-Cola in late summer of 1999 and were an immediate hit. As a result of advanced publicity in the Cavanagh Coca-Cola Collectors Society newsletter, World of Coca-Cola was inundated with requests before the toys ever arrived.

COCA-COLA EXCLUSIVE SET OF 4 1999

Issued 1999/Retired 2000

#0269   Polar Bear in Hooded Sweatshirt

#0272   Red Coca-Cola Disk

#0273   Seal in Delivery Outfit

#0274   Polar Bear in Serving Jacket and Hat

Price Guide: $40–50 Polar Bear in Hooded Sweatshirt, $10–12 Red Disk; rest $15 each

All have the exclusive Everything Coca-Cola second tags. The paws of the polar bears holding the Coca-Cola bottle finally are twisted up instead of down giving the impression the bear is about to take a swig of the "real thing."

The Cavanagh newsletter incorrectly pictured the #0274 Polar Bear in Serving Jacket and Hat as having a red vest and no bowtie, causing a lot of confusion. The final version is beautifully detailed with his black bowtie and smart white jacket with red satin trim.

Most popular in this set is the "Property of Coca-Cola" #0269 Polar Bear in Hooded Sweatshirt, the first to retire in early 2000. His gray velour sweatshirt immediately attracted collectors. Since all four stores sold out, prices for this special bear have shot up to $40–50.

The seal in this set is wearing a fancy green-and-white-striped jacket with a big red Coca-Cola disk on the back. His green delivery cap with red Coke button and red bowtie makes him the most intricately dressed thus far.

But the most unique member of this set is the red Coca-Cola Disc, marking the first time the Company has made a real bag of beans! The shiny red fabric in a disc shape bears the familiar Coca-Cola bottle logo on both sides.

COCA-COLA EXCLUSIVE GIFT SET OF 4 1999

Issued 1999/Retired 2000

#0195   Polar Bear in Holiday Pattern Vest (boy)

#0196   Polar Bear in Jumper (girl)

#0197   Seal in Nightshirt and Cap

#0198   Polar Bear in Nightshirt and Cap

Price Guide: $15 each

COCA-COLA EXCLUSIVE
SET OF 4 1999

COCA-COLA EXCLUSIVE GIFT SET OF 4 1999

These whimsical holiday visitors arrived a year later than expected. Originally planned to be released the previous Christmas as part of a set of six, production problems forced cancellation when the bean bag toys could not arrive by December. (Only the Formal Pair from this set was released, as an exclusive pair at World of Coca-Cola.)

All the members of this set sport exclusive Everything Coca-Cola double tags and various colors of holiday gift fabric. Bottles of Coke with ribbons, wrapped packages, candy canes and stockings are interspersed between repeats of the trademark Coca-Cola. They were quickly dubbed the "Exclusive Gift" set.

The first pair from this set is dressed to party with red satin jackets and jumpers. The other pair is ready for bed with nightshirts and stocking caps. Both pairs were a natural fit for collecting and holiday gift giving.

This set went through only one production run, and remaining supplies are limited on all four issues at Everything Coca-Cola stores. A few secondary market sources carry this exclusive set, and individual bean bags appear in Internet auctions regularly.

2nd ANNUAL COKE COLLECTORS CLASSIC BEAR 1999
Issued 1999/Retired 1999
#0304   1999 Collector Classic Polar Bear
Price Guide: $20–25

Coke fans were ready for the second annual Collectors Classic event held only at the World of Coca-Cola in Atlanta. On October 16, 1999, the doors flew open and anxious customers rushed in to purchase this exclusive polar bear and matching event bottle available only that day.

Just 2,160 bears were made, and they

sold out quickly. This bear, dressed in a yellow T-shirt, joined the first event edition as a collector favorite. Prices are steadily rising as fewer and fewer remain available for sale on the secondary market. Internet auctions bring $15–25 apiece.

ZOO ATLANTA PANDA BEARS 1999

Issued 1999/Retired 2000

#0322   Exclusive Krogers/Zoo Atlanta
         Panda Bear

#0323   Exclusive World of Coca-Cola
         Panda Bear

*Price Guide: $10-20 Kroger edition; $20–25
World of Coca-Cola edition*

Celebrating a different kind of event, two exclusive panda bean bags arrived to com-memorate the new Coca-Cola-sponsored Giant Panda exhibit at Zoo Atlanta in the fall of 1999.

The first release panda is exclusive to Zoo Atlanta and Kroger stores and comes with a double exclusive tag — the regular Cavanagh tag #322 and a second Kroger/Zoo Atlanta tag. Wearing a red T-shirt with a Zoo Atlanta patch on the sleeve and a bottle of Coke in its right paw, this bear is easy to distinguish from the second edition.

2nd ANNUAL COKE COLLEC-TORS CLASSIC BEAR 1999

Prices fluctuated on this first edition when the Zoo and Kroger stores sold out in the first few weeks following the arrival of the real pandas. More panda bean bags appeared in stores in early 2000, but supplies didn't last long.

The second edition could only be pur-chased from World of Coca-Cola Atlanta. It is distinguished by the Cavanagh tag #323 and an exclusive Everything Coca-Cola red tag. Just twenty-four hundred were made for the event. After selling out quickly from the Atlanta store, its price continues to rise on the secondary market.

The second edition has a smaller face, larger black patches around its eyes and no white patches on its feet. It more closely resembles the panda bear made for the Inter-national Bean Bag Collection (to be dis-cussed in a later chapter).

If you are planning a visit to Atlanta or Las Vegas, don't miss a trip to the Everything Coca-Cola store. The future of the Everything Coca-Cola stores should cause prices to rise on all World of Coca-Cola exclusive editions in the coming months, giving you even more of an excuse to make a trip.

Everyone loves the giant polar bear in the lobby of the Everything Coca-Cola store in Atlanta and Las Vegas. Sit on his lap for a photo . . . but watch out for a surprise.

Even if you are just passing through the Atlanta airport, you can stop by the little Everything Coca-Cola store.

(Refer to Appendix B for an address list of all the Everything Coca-Cola stores.)

ZOO ATLANTA PANDA BEARS 1999

CHAPTER 7

Cavanagh Coca-Cola Collectors Society

"Stay merry, refresh with Coke"
— 1964 advertising copy

The Cavanagh Coca-Cola Collectors Society (CCCC Society) is operated by Cavanagh Group International (CGI). It was started in 1993 to help collectors share their passion for Coca-Cola collectibles, especially Christmas collectibles. Dee Dukes, wife of company founder, John Cavanagh, serves as president.

One of the objectives of the society is to provide a sense of family by sharing member photos and stories in its newsletter. Mutual interest in collecting Coca-Cola memorabilia creates strong bonds, and getting advance notice of upcoming products makes members feel like "insiders."

One of the best sources of information for diehard Coca-Cola brand bean bag plush collectors is the society. Quarterly newsletters often have special previews of new editions and information about where to purchase them. An annual Coca-Cola brand Christmas Collectibles catalog also gives information on product lines and retail sources. The catalog lists bean bags by style number and name as well as the stores that carry the different lines by state and city.

The annual membership of $25 ($35 outside the U.S.) includes a personalized certificate, wallet card, free gifts for signing up, a quarterly newsletter full of great information about Coca-Cola collectibles, and special pieces created exclusively for the Society only available for purchase by current members.

Applications for membership can be made directly to the CCCC Society by letter, phone, or online at the Cavanagh Website. Many Heritage dealers also serve as Society Redemption Centers and can help you join and redeem members-only certificates for additional items. A list is published for members every year and can be accessed on the Website or by phoning the society.

In recognition of the booming passion for Coca-Cola brand bean bag plush, the Cavanagh Coca-Cola Collectors Society announced it would offer its first exclusive bean bag to members who signed up for the club in 1998.

CCCC SOCIETY

1998 EXCLUSIVE

Issued 1998/Retired 1998

#0151 Polar Bear in Green

Sweater with Red Reindeer Logo

Price Guide: $75–150

The CCCC Society's first exclusive bean bag drew new members in droves. With a limited production of twenty-five thousand pieces, available only to members, Coca-Cola brand bean bag plush collectors signed up to have this special polar bear.

Once supplies were exhausted, the secondary market began booming. Internet

CCCC SOCIETY 1998 EXCLUSIVE

sales of this society bear are always brisk with prices ranging from $35 to $40 in mid-1999 to $60 to $70 by 2000. Sources for this bear are few and far between.

The CCCC Society offered even more goodies in 1999. Membership included an exclusive bean bag with director's chair, and, for the first time, members also could order the fifty-first critter in the International Collection: Totanca the Buffalo, representing the USA. (See Chapter 8, International Bean Bag Collection, for more information.)

CCCC SOCIETY 1999 EXCLUSIVE
Issued 1999/Retired 1999
#0126 Polar Bear with Polka Dot Collar "A Collector Society Exclusive"
Price Guide: $30–50

This polar bear comes with a red ribbon and polka dot collar sitting on its own red director's chair. Keeping the old face polar bear, so loved by collectors, proved to be a great boon to the CCCC Society. Coke collectors had to have it, and membership swelled.

As Cavanagh completes the 1999 membership redemption for this polar bear in director's chair, CCCC SOCIETY 1999 EXCLUSIVE more and more are showing up on Internet auctions for sale at escalating prices.

CCCC SOCIETY TOTANCA

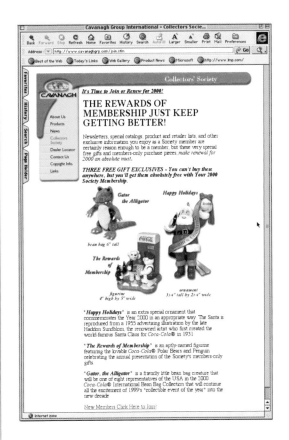

Totanca the Buffalo, offered to members for purchase, also was a definite must-have for anyone owning the International Bean Bag Collection of fifty animals.

Building on success, the CCCC Society is offering two new International Bean Bag animals for 2000 Society members.

Free with membership application or renewal is Gator the Alligator from the USA. Member kits also contain an exclusive Santa 2000 ornament and Polar Bear Cubs figurine, "Rewards of Membership." That's three free gifts with the 2000 membership alone.

Members also will receive a special certificate that allows them to redeem a second exclusive member of the International Bean Bag Collection: Possy the Opossum, also representing the USA.

Photos and further descriptions of these additional members of the International Bean Bag Collection can be found in the next chapter.

For more information about the Cavanagh CCCC Society, see Appendix B.

CHAPTER 8

International Bean Bags

"I'd like to buy the world a Coke"
— 1971 jingle

BROEL TOWERS, KORTRIJK, BELGIUM

I n the boldest move yet, Coca-Cola introduced the International Bean Bag Collection for 1999. Full color advertisements proclaim, "Coca-Cola Celebrates its Family of Countries Around the World."

Today, in virtually every corner of the globe, generations of families, friends and neighbors can join together to enjoy a Coke. Right now, Coke is served in more than two hundred countries and on every continent on earth. The new Coca-Cola International Bean Bag Collection celebrates the Coca-Cola family of

MOMBASA, KENYA

nations with arguably the most lovable bean bags ever offered.

Featuring animals representing fifty countries, the International Bean Bag Collection is by far the most ambitious undertaking by CGI. The special

1999 SET 1, #0213, DOVER THE BULLDOG, GREAT BRITAIN

holographic swing tag that comes with each critter lists its name, facts about the country it represents and its style number. The tush tag is the national flag of the country. Of course, each animal is holding a bottle of Coca-Cola, some labeled in the national language of its homeland.

Some of the bean bags look familiar to Coca-Cola collectors. Baltic the reindeer from Sweden (in the 1999 collection) looks very much like other reindeers released in other sets. Likewise, Howls the wolf from Romania resembles a previous husky edition. The remaining bean bags are new designs. Many animals had never before been produced in bean bag form by any company. Cuteness and authenticity were the main goals.

The International Bean Bag Collection is everything a collector could want:

- *Ongoing commitment by Coca-Cola.* Coca-Cola brand bean bag plush is here to stay and getting better with each release.

- *Limited production number.* Although the exact number of sets produced was not released in 1999, a one-time production run guarantees each bean bag animal is highly collectible. For the 2000 collection, CGI announced that production has been limited to thirty-five thousand of each set.

1999 SET 1, #0219,
MASA THE LION,
MOZAMBIQUE

1999 SET 2, #0228,
ZONGSHI
THE PANDA,
CHINA

- *Immediate retirement.* On the first of a selected month, and the first of each selected month thereafter, the International Collection sets arrive and retire the same day. Each retailer only gets one shipment of each set.

- *Limited retail sources.* Sold only through the twenty-two hundred Heritage Dealers, each store receives a pre-determined allocation without the possibility of re-ordering. Once sold out, they are gone forever.

- *Unique design.* From the holographic swing tag to prevent counterfeiting, to the tush tag with a flag of the bean bag's respective country, to the intricate design of each animal, this collection is unique in all the bean bag world.

1999 INTERNATIONAL COCA-COLA BEAN BAG COLLECTION
by set, style number, name and country

Set 1	Set 2	Set 3	Set 4	Set 5
Retired April 1	Retired June 1	Retired August 1	Retired October 1	Retired December 1
Eagle #0211 Reegle United States	Pelican #0221 Can Can Cuba	Tapir #0231 Taps Venezuela	Zebra #0241 Topus Nigeria	Coki Frog #0251 Hopps Puerto Rico
Toucan #0212 Toolu Honduras	Reindeer #0222 Baltic Sweden	Black Rhinoceros #0232 Rhiny Tanzania	Walrus #0242 Waller Greenland	Penguin #0252 Peng Chili
Bulldog #0213 Dover Great Britain	Iguana #0223 Paco Mexico	Moose #0233 Gourmand Canada	Llama #0243 Laffs Bolivia	Rabbit #0253 Lochs Scotland
Poodle #0214 Strudel France	Giraffe #0224 Rifraff Somalia	Wild Boar #0234 Lors Italy	Sheep #0244 Woolsy Ireland	Proboscis Monkey #0254 Neppy Thailand
Bull #0215 Toro Spain	Baboon #0225 Croon Pakistan	Brown Bear #0235 Barris Russia	Crocodile #0245 Crunch Sudan	Hippopotamus #0255 Meeska Zambia
Bengal Tiger #0216 Curry India	Sea Turtle #0226 Salty Bahamas	Yak #0236 Waks Nepal	Wolf #0246 Howls Romania	St. Bernard #0256 Nardie Switzerland
Elephant #0217 Clomp Kenya	Longhorn Cow #0227 Vaca Argentina	Snow Monkey #0237 Key Key Japan	Orangutan #0247 Orany Singapore	Kiwi #0257 Kelp New Zealand
Gorilla #0218 Rilly Rwanda	Panda #0228 Zongshi China	Camel #0238 Ramel Egypt	Aardvark #0248 Ardie Niger	Octopus #0258 Oppy Greece
Lion #0219 Masa Mozambique	Parrot #0229 Barrot Brazil	Peacock #0239 Pock Sri Lanka	Cheetah #0249 Heeta Nambia	Jackal #0259 Streak Tunisia
Koala #0220 Quala Australia	Fox #0230 Fannie Germany	Badger #0240 Badgey Czech Republic	Pot Belly Pig #0250 Blubby Vietnam	Ostrich #0260 Masha South Africa

- *Names*. For the first time, Coca-Cola brand bean bag plush toys have more than style numbers and descriptions. Each animal has a special name reflecting the country from which it comes.
- *Mint condition swing tags*. A custom-designed, bottle cap-shaped clear tag protector, installed at the factory before shipment for the 1999 set, has not been available anywhere else.
- *Reasonable price*. At the suggested retail price of $7.99, everyone can afford to collect all fifty.
- *High investment potential*. With the limited availability and immediate retirement, the International Bean Bag Collection appears to have the greatest potential for increasing value.

1999 SET 3, #0239, POCK THE PEACOCK, SRI LANKA

ALTERNATIVE NAMES FOR CANADIAN RELEASES

Set	Animal	Style #	Name	Country	Canadian Name
1	Toucan	#0212	Toolu	Honduras	Toulu
2	Fox	#0230	Fannie	Germany	After the Fox
3	Black Rhinoceros	#0232	Rhiny	Tanzania	Belo the Rhino
	Brown Bear	#0235	Barris	Russia	Baris the Bear
4	Zebra	#0241	Topus	Nigeria	Zeb
	Llama	#0243	Laffs	Bolivia	Loafer
	Sheep	#0244	Woolsy	Ireland	Woolsey
	Wolf	#0246	Howls	Romania	Streak
	Pot Belly Pig	#0250	Blubby	Vietnam	Bella
5	Proboscis Monkey	#0254	Neppy	Thailand	Popo
	Hippopotamus	#0255	Meeska	Zambia	Amos
	Kiwi	#0257	Kelp	New Zealand	Wiki
	Octopus	#0258	Oppy	Greece	Otto
	Jackal	#0259	Streak	Tunisia	Kackal
	Ostrich	#0260	Masha	South Africa	Stich

To promote "the collecting opportunity of 1999" CGI used print advertising and television and in-store promotions. The hobby media also covered the release. *Mary Beth's Beanie World* magazine issued a special forty-eight-page edition dedicated solely to the International Bean Bag Collection. With color photos and descriptions of all fifty animals, the excitement was building for the big day when the first set would be released.

A week before the first shipments were sent to retailers, a special Coca-Cola segment on QVC introduced the International Bean Bag Collection to millions of viewers. Limited numbers of Set 1 sold for a special price during the broadcast.

Collectors were poised to grab up the first set. Some stores took advance reserva-

1999 SET 4, #0244 WOOLSY, IRELAND

tions on the entire collection. Pre-sales even began popping up on the Internet.

From start to finish, the ambitious International Bean Bag Collection proved to be a difficult feat for Cavanagh to pull off. Negotiating the complicated world of international trademarks offered many challenges. Names, perfectly acceptable in the United States, were already trademarked in Canada, forcing several animals to be renamed for the Canadian market.

This caused a real headache in production (getting the right name on the right animal) and distribution (getting the Canadian editions to Canada and not the United States).

To make matters more difficult, several of the Coca-Cola bottles came printed in the language of the country. Not only did the

1999 SET 5, #0252, PENG, CHILE

swing tags and hang tags have to match the animal, the Coke bottles had to match as well.

There were plenty of problems at home. Trying to ship out the entire stock of International Bean Bag Collection to retailers across the United States and Canada in a two-week period brought Cavanagh's shipping department to a near standstill.

1999 SET 1, #0211, REEGLE, USA

But for all the first-year kinks, collectors loved the International Bean Bag Collection and purchased them in record numbers. Hundreds of new Coca-Cola bean bag collectors joined the ranks wanting every other edition made. Reegle the Eagle became one of the most sought-after toys in the bean bag world, hitting the hobby media's "top ten" charts week after week.

Adding to the fun of collecting, Coca-Cola created exclusive accessories to accompany the International Bean Bag Collection. A ten-slot crate, metal Coca-Cola soda fountain table and chair, metal bicycle, bench with metal back, and a swinging chair all added drama to displaying the collection. Other accessories include a red wooden six-pack, sleigh, hanging vinyl holder, sling chair, director's chair, park bench and wooden crate.

And that's not all that's exciting. Totanca is the fifty-first and most desired member of the 1999 International Bean Bag collection. Totanca the buffalo represents the United States. His swing tag states: "As the buffalo roamed the American plains in 1886, Dr. Pemberton was busy creating the world's most famous soft drink, Coca-Cola. Today, the two share the role of great American icons."

Only 1999 members of the Cavanagh Coca-Cola Collectors Society received a certificate to purchase this limited edition bean bag at Heritage

Redemption Centers. And new members joined en masse to get this limited edition treasure.

Announced for 2000 is a new International Bean Bag Collection.

The 2000 Collection offers twenty-four new bean bag animals released in four sets. Each set contains animals representing five different countries and one USA bean bag.

Like the previous editions, each of these charming animals has its own special name, carries its national flag on the tush tag and a has a bottle of Coca-Cola on its paw, wing, flipper or hoof.

The beautiful holographic swing tags have a newly designed clear tag protector (that locks tighter so it doesn't fall off). These tags are designed with banking encryption technology to guarantee authenticity and prevent counterfeiting. This time, the tag protectors will not come from the

2000 SOCIETY
MEMBERS ONLY,
TOTANCA,
USA

INTERNATIONAL
COLLECTION
ACCESSORIES

factories on the tags, but retailers have to purchase protectors separately and attach themselves.   Undoubtedly many tags will be damaged in shipping, and many retailers will not be saddled with the added expense and bother.

Each animal is limited to thirty-five thousand pieces. New packaging for the 2000 International Collection should make the animals even more popular: Each set of six will come in a specially created six-pack carrier featuring Coke logos and colorful flags from the six countries represented in each set. Each carrier will be designed specifically for each set.

Dates scheduled for release and retirement are: June 1, August 1, October 1, and December 1. Cavanagh representatives promise that this time each set will truly be introduced and retired on the same day.

Finding a Heritage Dealer that has the 2000 International Bean Bag Collection will be harder than before. All dealers who can-

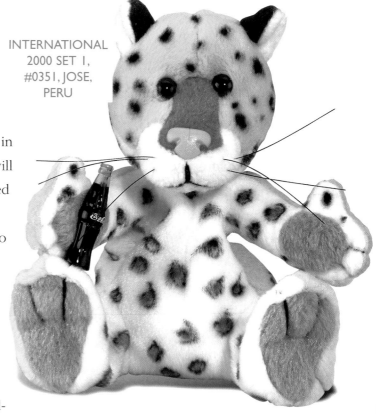

INTERNATIONAL 2000 SET 1, #0351, JOSE, PERU

celed orders, or dropped out before the entire collection was released, are not going to be allowed to order any 2000 editions. Each qualified Heritage Dealer will receive only a pre-determined number of sets. No reorders are possible.

For the 2000 members of the Cavanagh Coca-Cola Christmas Society, there will be two new International Bean Bag Collection members.

Gator the Alligator represents the USA as

INTERNATIONAL 2000 SET 2, #0357, RINGER, PORTUGAL

Set 1	Set 2	Set 3	Set 4
Swan #0330 Sailor Austria	Flamingo #0322 Mingo Morocco	Skunk #0341 Odes USA	Flying Squirrel #0334 Freddie Zaire
Mandarin Duck #0333 Duckles Taiwan	Hedgehog #0339 Baccy Wales	Rooster #0342 Cockles Malaysia	Grizzly Bear #0335 Grizzy USA
Flying Dragon #0343 Fire Indonesia	Anteater #0346 Anty Paraguay	Mouflon Sheep #0344 Shep Slovakia	Fruit Bat #0336 Batts Angola
Killer Whale #0345 Tides Norway	Wild Pony #0353 Apache USA	Scarlet Macaw #0358 Cawcaw Columbia	Northern Hawk Owl #0338 Hooty Lithuania
Jaguar #0351 Jose Peru	Lammergeier #0354 Lammer Ukraine	White Stork #0363 Hans Netherlands	Arctic Fox #0350 Whitey Finland
Raccoon #0365 Crooner USA	Small Spotted Genet #0357 Ringer Portugal	River Otter #0364 Otties Poland	Puffin #0356 Eire Northern Ireland

INTERNATIONAL
2000 SET 3,
#0342, COCKLES,
MALAYSIA

the twenty-fifth member of the 2000 International Bean Bag Collection. He will be one of eight animals representing the USA in the 2000 Collection. Cavanagh refers to the gator in advance publicity as "not scary at all, but a friendly little creature."

Members also will receive a special certificate that allows them to redeem a second exclusive member of the International Bean Bag Collection: Possy the Opossum, representing the USA. Only one exclusive bean bag is allowed per member and supplies are limited.

INTERNATIONAL 2000 SET 4, #0336, BATTS, ANGOLA

Member information states: "Few animals are more prolific or American than Opossums, so who better than Possy to help represent the USA in the 2000 continuation of the Coca-Cola International Bean Bag Collection."

Success of this latest set will determine if new editions will be released in coming years, but based on the continuing demand, our guess is yes.

CCCC SOCIETY
2000 EXCLUSIVE
#0347, GATOR,
USA
*Price Guide:
Estimate
$25–35 each*

CCCC SOCIETY
2000 EXCLUSIVE
#0367, POSSY,
USA
*Price Guide:
Estimate
$25–35 each*

INTERNATIONAL 2000 SET 2, #0339, BACCY, WALES

INTERNATIONAL 2000 SET 1, #0333, DUCKLES, TAIWAN

INTERNATIONAL 2000 SET 3, #0344, SHEP, SLOVAKIA

INTERNATIONAL 2000 SET 4, #0350, WHITEY, FINLAND

1999 International

Bean Bags

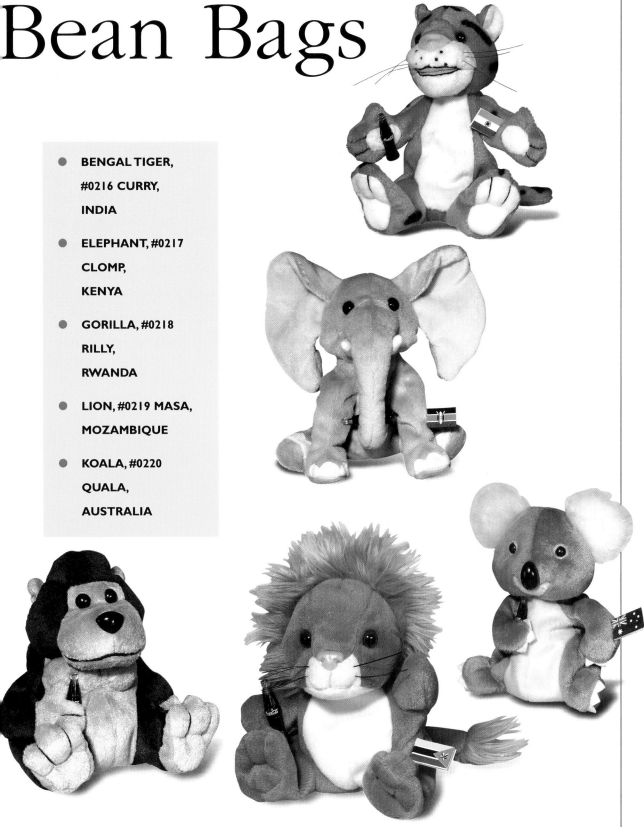

- **BENGAL TIGER, #0216 CURRY, INDIA**

- **ELEPHANT, #0217 CLOMP, KENYA**

- **GORILLA, #0218 RILLY, RWANDA**

- **LION, #0219 MASA, MOZAMBIQUE**

- **KOALA, #0220 QUALA, AUSTRALIA**

SET 2

Suggested Retail $7.99 each

- **PELICAN, #0221**
  CAN CAN,
  CUBA
- **REINDEER, #0222**
  BALTIC
  SWEDEN
- **IGUANA, #0223**
  PACO
  MEXICO
- **GIRAFFE, #0224**
  RIFRAFF
  SOMALIA
- **BABOON, #0225**
  CROON
  PAKISTAN

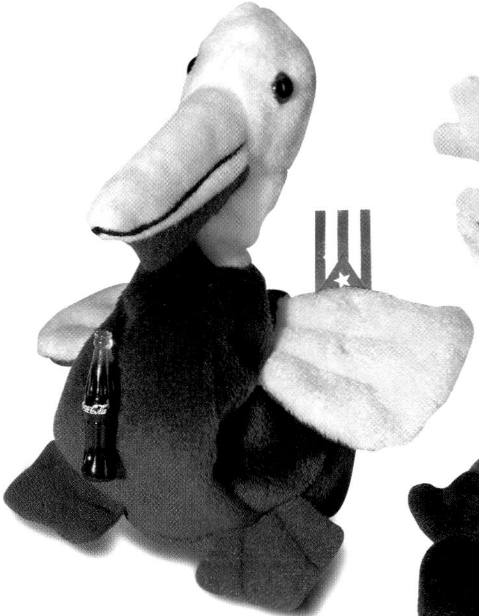

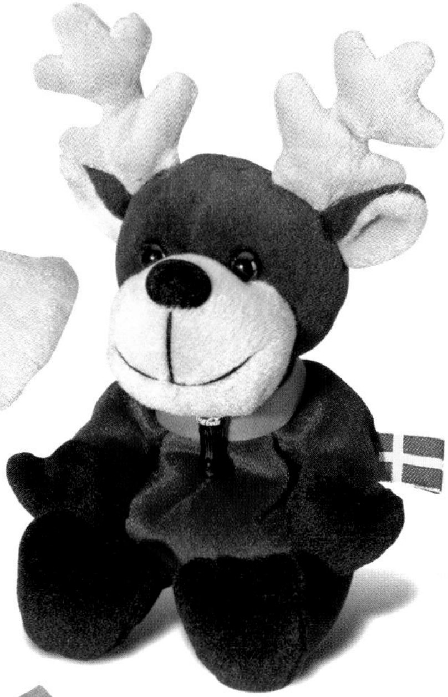

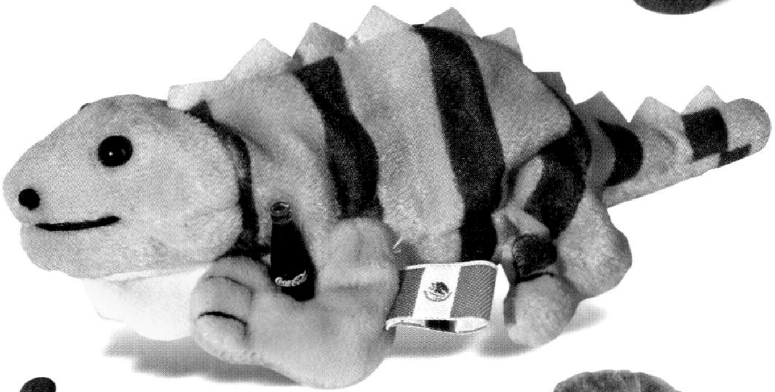

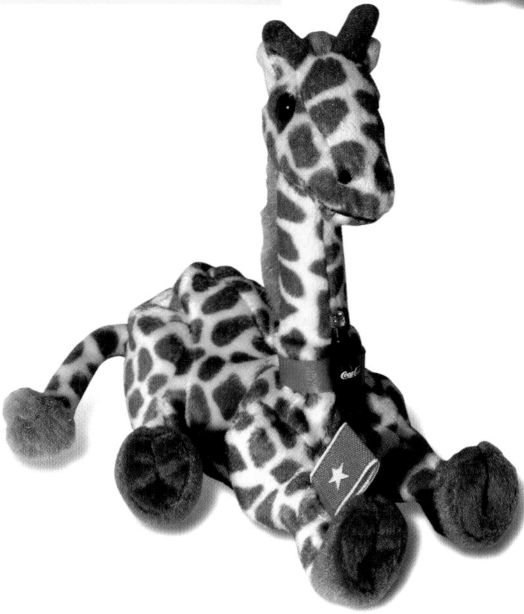

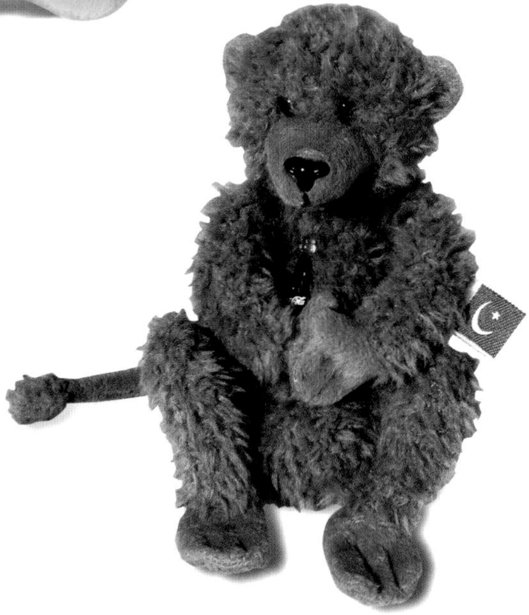

- **SEA TURTLE, #0226**
  SALTY
  BAHAMAS

- **LONGHORN**
  COW, #0227
  VACA
  ARGENTINA

- **PARROT, #0229**
  BARROT
  BRAZIL

- **FOX, #0230**
  FANNIE
  GERMANY

- **PANDA, #0228**
  ZONGSHI
  CHINA

Suggested Retail $7.99 each

- **TAPIR, #0231**
  TAPS
  VENEZUELA

- **BLACK**
  RHINOCEROS,
  #0232
  RHINY
  TANZANIA

- **MOOSE, #0233**
  GOURMAND
  CANADA

- **WILD BOAR,**
  #0234
  LORS
  ITALY

- **BROWN BEAR, #0235**
  BARRIS
  RUSSIA

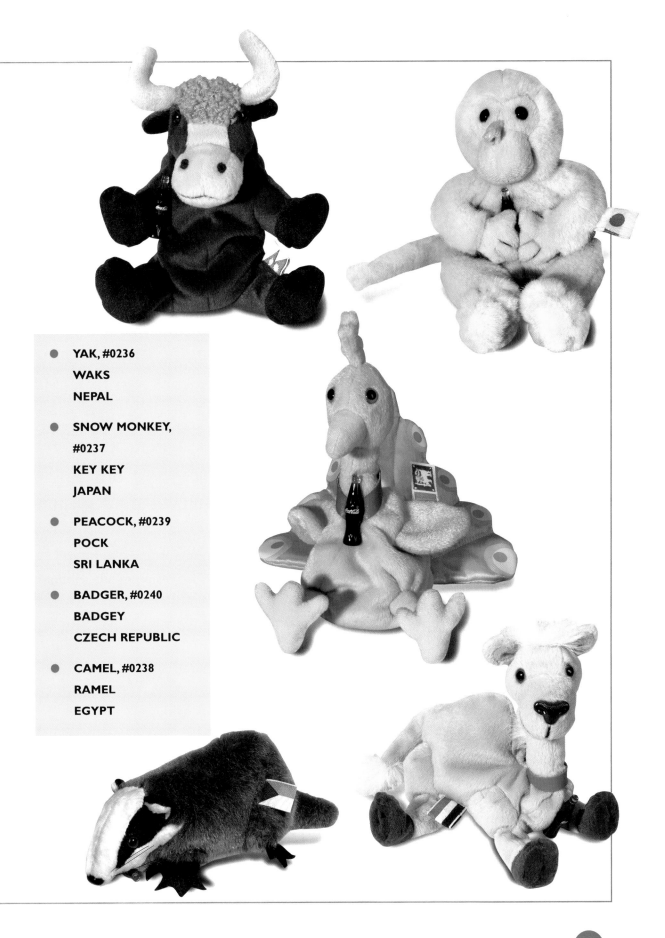

- YAK, #0236
  WAKS
  NEPAL

- SNOW MONKEY,
  #0237
  KEY KEY
  JAPAN

- PEACOCK, #0239
  POCK
  SRI LANKA

- BADGER, #0240
  BADGEY
  CZECH REPUBLIC

- CAMEL, #0238
  RAMEL
  EGYPT

SET 4

uggested Retail $7.99 each

- **WALRUS, #0242**
  WALLER
  GREENLAND

- **ZEBRA, #0241**
  TOPUS
  NIGERIA

- **LLAMA, #0243**
  LAFFS
  BOLIVIA

- **CROCODILE, #0245**
  CRUNCH
  SUDAN

- **SHEEP, #0244**
  WOOLSY
  IRELAND

- **WOLF, #0246**
  HOWLS
  ROMANIA

- **ORANGUTAN, #0247**
  ORANY
  SINGAPORE

- **CHEETAH, #0249**
  HEETA
  NAMBIA

- **AARDVARK, #0248**
  ARDIE
  NIGER

- **POT BELLY PIG,**
  #0250
  BLUBBY
  VIETNAM

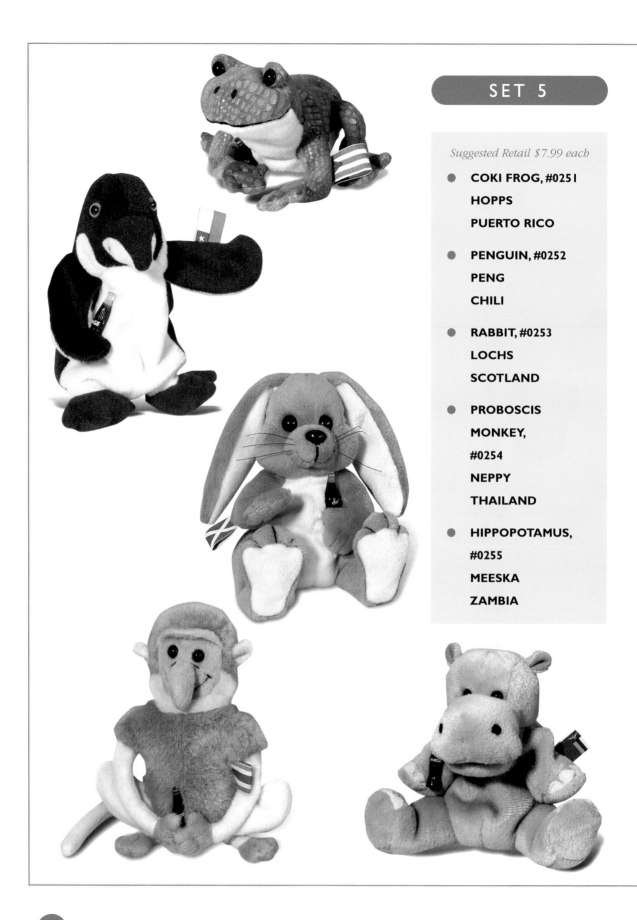

Suggested Retail $7.99 each

- **COKI FROG, #0251**
  HOPPS
  PUERTO RICO

- **PENGUIN, #0252**
  PENG
  CHILI

- **RABBIT, #0253**
  LOCHS
  SCOTLAND

- **PROBOSCIS**
  MONKEY,
  #0254
  NEPPY
  THAILAND

- **HIPPOPOTAMUS,**
  #0255
  MEESKA
  ZAMBIA

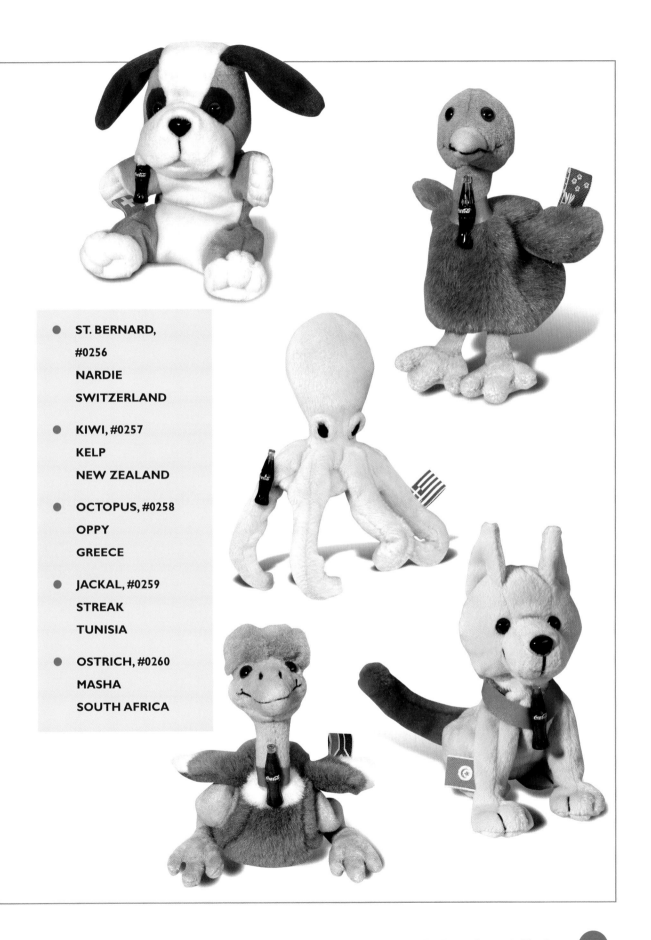

- **ST. BERNARD, #0256**
  NARDIE
  SWITZERLAND

- **KIWI, #0257**
  KELP
  NEW ZEALAND

- **OCTOPUS, #0258**
  OPPY
  GREECE

- **JACKAL, #0259**
  STREAK
  TUNISIA

- **OSTRICH, #0260**
  MASHA
  SOUTH AFRICA

2000 International

Suggested Retail $7.99 each

- **MANDARIN DUCK,** #0333 **DUCKLES TAIWAN**

- **SWAN, #0330 SAILOR AUSTRIA**

- **JAGUAR, #0351 JOSE PERU**

- **FLYING DRAGON,** #0343 FIRE **INDONESIA**

- **KILLER WHALE,** #0345 **TIDES NORWAY**

- **RACCOON, #0365 CROONER USA**

Bean Bags

Suggested Retail $7.99 each

- **FLAMINGO, #0332**
  MINGO
  MOROCCO

- **HEDGEHOG, #0339**
  BACCY
  WALES

- **ANTEATER, #0346**
  ANTY
  PARAGUAY

- **WILD PONY, #0353**
  APACHE
  USA

- **LAMMERGEIER,**
  #0354
  LAMMER
  UKRAINE

- **SMALL SPOTTED**
  GENET
  #0357
  RINGER
  PORTUGAL

Suggested Retail $7.99 each

- **SKUNK, #0341**
  ODES
  USA

- **MOUFLON SHEEP,**
  #0344
  SHEP
  SLOVAKIA

- **ROOSTER, #0342**
  COCKLES
  MALAYSIA

- **SCARLET MACAW,**
  #0358
  CAWCAW
  COLUMBIA

- **RIVER OTTER, #0364**
  OTTIES
  POLAND

- **WHITE STORK, #0363**
  HANS
  NETHERLANDS

SET 4

Suggested Retail $7.99 each

- **FLYING SQUIRREL, #0334 FREDDIE ZAIRE**

- **GRIZZLY BEAR, #0335 GRIZZY USA**

- **FRUIT BAT, #0336 BATTS ANGOLA**

- **NORTHERN HAWK OWL, #0338 HOOTY LITHUANIA**

- **ARCTIC FOX, #0350 WHITEY FINLAND**

- **PUFFIN, #0356 EIRE NORTHERN IRELAND**

CHAPTER 9

NASCAR Bean Bags

"Stop for a pause, Go refreshed"
— 1937 advertising copy

Coca-Cola has been a part of NASCAR excitement for thirty years. First associated with sponsoring such legendary drivers as Bobby Allison, Coca-Cola increased its involvement in the past fifteen years by sponsoring several annual NASCAR events such as the Coca-Cola 600 at Charlotte Motor Speedway.

In 1998, Coca-Cola became the "Official Soft Drink of NASCAR" in a multi-million-dollar deal that opened up a new avenue to collectors. The Coca-Cola Racing Family includes some of the hottest drivers on NASCAR's Winston Cup circuit: #3 Dale Earnhardt Sr., #8 Dale Earnhardt Jr., #88 Dale Jarrett, #94 Bill Elliott, #44 Kyle

Petty, #18 Bobby Labonte, #99 Jeff Burton, #1 Steve Park and #20 Tony Stewart. Busch Grand National circuit drivers who have raced under Coca-Cola sponsorship are: #88 Jason Jarrett and #45 Adam Petty.

The fastest growing spectator sport, NASCAR has long produced highly collectible driver memorabilia, from die-cast cars to racing jackets and caps. To the thrill of both Coca-Cola bean bag plush collectors and NASCAR fans, a new line of NASCAR bean bags was introduced by Cavanagh in 1999.

1999 NASCAR DRIVER BEARS

#18 Bobby Labonte

#20 Tony Stewart

#28 Kenny Irwin

#44 Kyle Petty

#45 Adam Petty

#18 BOBBY LABONTE, 1999 SET

#88 Dale Jarrett

#94 Bill Elliott

#99 Jeff Burton

Price Guide: $60–80 a set; $8 each

The NASCAR set, announced to Heritage dealers early in 1999, was advertised to include ten of the top NASCAR Racing Family drivers. Prototype sets shown to gift store owners at a trade show in January included all nine Winston Cup drivers and Dale Earnhardt Jr., then a star of the Busch series. Two additional bean bags were to be sold separately: Dale Sr. and Jr. in black zippered jackets.

From the start there were problems involving multiple trademarks and legal agreements. In NASCAR, every team is treated as a separate company with its own trademarked name, official racing number, colors and sponsors. Agreements had to be worked out with each

#20 TONY STEWART, 1999 SET

driver individually, then with each driver's sponsoring companies.

Delay followed delay as some drivers committed to the line while others did not. Some drivers agreed but sponsoring companies did not.

Finally, in the fall of 1999, the long-awaited NASCAR bean bag set arrived to the cheers of Coca-Cola and NASCAR fans. While the final set contained only eight drivers, and no special pair came out for the Earnhardts, it was worth the wait.

Highly detailed and very colorful, each NASCAR driver bear comes in a satin racing shirt in the driver's respective team colors. The official racing number and signature of the driver adorns the front. The back features the Coca-Cola Racing Family checkered bottle logo, and the sleeve is labeled with the "Official Soft Drink of NASCAR" logo.

Every bear features a unique round swing tag. The tag also is imprinted with the Coca-Cola Racing Family checkered bottle logo on the front, official racing number and signature of the driver on the inside right

#28 KENNY IRWIN, 1999 SET

panel, and all those trademark notices (unique to each driver) on the left inside panel.

These colorful NASCAR bears, as expected, were an instant hit. As triple-interest collectibles (Coca-Cola, NASCAR and bean bags), they appeared at Heritage Dealer stores across the country for just a short time.

2000 NASCAR DRIVER BEARS
Price Guide: Estimate $8–10 each

Exciting new NASCAR bean bag collectibles are planned to come in 2000. Although rumors of a father-son pair featur-

#44 KYLE PETTY, 1999 SET

#99 JEFF BURTON, 1999 SET

ing Dale Sr. and Jr. proved untrue, additional bear bean bags representing new drivers are on the drawing board.

The tentative starting lineup for the 2000

#88 DALE JARRETT, 1999 SET

Coca-Cola Racing Family includes: Tony Stewart, Dale Earnhardt Sr., Dale Earnhardt Jr., Dale Jarrett, Kyle Petty, Bill Elliott, Steve Park, Bobby Labonte and Jeff Burton.

#94 BILL ELLIOTT, 1999 SET

MARY MEYERS RED LINE BEANIE RACERS

Dale Earnhardt Sr.

Dale Earnhardt Jr.

Price Guide: $25 each

In a separate deal with Action Performance Companies, Inc., Coca-Cola authorized production of a totally different kind of bean bag toy: bean bag cars known as Red Line Beanie Racers. Dale Earnhardt Sr. and Jr. cars were released, commemorating the NASCAR Thunder Special Motegi Coca-Cola 500 held in Motegi City, Japan, on November 22, 1998. Father and son raced against each other for the first time in the event.

EARNHARDT
BEANIE RACER

This head-to-head battle between the Earnhardts featured the most beautifully designed Coca-Cola cars. Dale Sr.'s Monte Carlo, painted bright red, has the Coca-Cola Racing Family logo on the hood of his famous No. 3. Dale Jr.'s Monte Carlo, painted black, features the Coca-Cola polar bear drinking a Coke logo on his No. 1 car.

This race proliferated hundreds of items from die-cast collector cars to matching helmets to racing jackets to T-shirts, all with the special insignias for Coca-Cola.

The bean bag toys are easily distinguished from other bean bag racers because they are larger (eight inches long) at 1:24 scale. They are made of durable vinyl that allows more detailed colors and graphics than plush fabric. Twenty thousand bean bag toys were produced of each car, a limited enough number to justify collectibility. Each racer is hand-numbered and gift-boxed.

Red Liners are available at fine gift and collectible stores as well as at NASCAR-sponsored events. If you are unable to find a store in your area, call 1-888-758-2327, or check out Internet stores that specialize in selling Coca-Cola and NASCAR collectibles.

CHAPTER 10

The Coca-Cola Collectors Club Editions

"Thirst asks nothing more."
— 1938 slogan

Bringing together Coca-Cola collectors from around the world, The Coca-Cola Collectors Club (TCCCC) is a non-profit organization "for collectors and their families who are interested in the history and memorabilia of The Coca-Cola Company."

With a membership now in the thousands, TCCCC provides a fun place for people to share their hobby excitement and trade and sell collectibles, not to mention get the latest inside information.

Formerly called the "Cola Clan," TCCCC is not sponsored by The Coca-Cola Company. Regional and local chapters, all run by volunteers, offer regular meetings, newsletters, special merchandise and opportunities to buy, sell or trade collectibles.

The group's annual national convention is the high point of the year for serious Coca-Cola collectors. Each convention features informative meetings, an awards dinner, live and silent auctions and the traditional "room hopping" (members open up their hotel rooms to show off their best and most unusual items in a swap meet atmosphere).

In 1997, regional TCCCC chapters began offering special Coca-Cola-authorized bean bag toys to commemorate various events, providing yet another niche for collectors. Produced in limited quantity and available almost solely to attending members, these special collector club editions are high on the lists of serious hobbyists.

Pricing is difficult since less than fifty of each toy are bought and sold each year. So prices can vary on Internet auctions from $50 to $450 depending on the number up for sale. Collectors want the first available, knowing they may be forced to wait a long time for the chance to buy another. Few retail stores provide the special event bean bags.

Not produced by CGI, special club editions must be approved by The Coca-Cola Company. When several local clubs hopped on the bean bag bandwagon without getting advance permission, Coca-Cola issued strict guidelines to curb the unauthorized use of its trademark.

Only legitimate chapters of The Coca-Cola Collectors Club can produce a special bean bag carrying the Coca-Cola name for an annual meeting or mini-convention. No merchandise can be made for personal use or profit. Only members of the TCCCC may receive the special bean bag at the event, with few exceptions.

In order to produce a special bean bag, the request is first sent to the legal department of The Coca-Cola Company for approval. A vendor approved by Coca-Cola offers a catalog of pre-designed bean bag animals to choose from. (Coca-Cola selects a specific vendor for each type of merchandise the club may wish to produce.) Then a T-shirt, or other accessory, is printed with the name of the sponsoring club, event location and date.

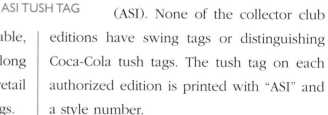

ASI TUSH TAG

The authorized vendors who can make these low-volume specialty bean bags are members of the Advertising Specialty Institute (ASI). None of the collector club editions have swing tags or distinguishing Coca-Cola tush tags. The tush tag on each authorized edition is printed with "ASI" and a style number.

ATLANTA CHAPTER TCCCC

CHRISTMAS MOOSE 1997

Issued 12/97 Quantity 140

Price Guide: $250—300

The first and hardest to find of the collector club editions is the Atlanta Chapter TCCCC Moose. Given only to members of this chapter who attended the annual Christmas

Party, no one outside the club knew much about it. Just 140 moose were made, each one wearing a red T-shirt with "1997 Atlanta Chapter TCCCC" printed on one side and "Enjoy Coca-Cola" printed on the other. The toy, with brown body and dark brown antlers made of plush fabric, can sit up or lie flat.

TCCCC ATLANTA CHAPTER CHRISTMAS MOOSE 1997

When the moose first turned up for resale on the Internet, most serious Coca-Cola bean bag collectors were unaware of its potential value and passed it by. Most became children's toys.

Still, from time to time, a moose will appear for auction or turn up elsewhere on the secondary market.

SPRINGTIME IN ATLANTA MOOSE 1998

Issued 4/98 Quantity 144
Price Guide $250–300

This second edition Coca-Cola moose was given out in children's gift packets to attendees at the 1998 Springtime in Atlanta® event, held April 8-11. The annual event, sponsored by the Atlanta Chapter of the TCCCC, is an anticipated mini-convention with the theme "Christmas in April."

Springtime in Atlanta originally specialized in Santa figures and Christmas collectibles based on the famous Coca-Cola

Santa, created by Haddon Sundblom for holiday sales campaigns beginning in the 1930s. ("Thirst Knows No Season.") But now the event showcases all kinds of Coca-Cola collectibles.

This moose is larger than the previous edition, is made from a fuzzy fabric never before seen in a bean bag and is very hard to find. The front of the red T-shirt states, "Enjoy Coca-Cola." On the back: "Celebration of Santa–Springtime in Atlanta April 8–11, 1998 TCCCC."

SPRINGTIME IN ATLANTA MOOSE 1998

MINNEAPOLIS TCCCC
ANNUAL CONVENTION FROG 1998

Issued 7/98 Quantity 400
Price Guide: $150–200

This special green "Coke" frog was available in the children's packet distributed at the 24th Annual National Coca-Cola Collectors Club Convention, held in Minneapolis in July of 1998.

Just four hundred of the frogs were made, and two hundred and fifty came in the children's packet. Fifty frogs also were sent to state chapters, and the remaining hundred sold in less than ten minutes at the TCCCC sales table during the convention.

The frog is a collector's prize. The shirt states "Enjoy Coca-Cola" on the back and "24th Annual Convention, The Coca-Cola Collectors Club, Minneapolis, MN, 1998" on the front.

TCCCC ATLANTA CHAPTER
CHRISTMAS TY DEER 1998

MINNEAPOLIS TCCCC
CONVENTION FROG 1998

ATLANTA CHAPTER TCCCC
CHRISTMAS PARTY TY DEER 1998

Issued 12/98 Quantity 120
Price Guide: $175–250

When Ty's Whisper the Deer was handed out at the Atlanta Chapter of the TCCCC for its annual Christmas party in 1998, it caused quite an uproar. Not produced by the authorized vendor, The Coca-Cola Company issued strict new guidelines prohibiting the use of "unauthorized" bean bags with the Coca-Cola trademark.

Just 120 were made, each wearing a white tee printed with "Atlanta Chapter Christmas 12/10/98 TCCCC" on the front and "Enjoy Coca-Cola" on the back. It has the Ty heart-shaped swing tag of Whisper the Deer.

Collectors initially backed far away from this questionable bean bag, wondering how a Ty "beanie baby" came to have a Coca-Cola T-shirt. As other collector club special editions began arriving on the scene, it gained greater acceptance and is now a much-wanted edition in any serious collection.

OHIO WINTERFEST TCCCC BEAR 1999

Issued 2/99 Quantity 150
Price Guide: $175–300

Breaking the mold for Collector Club

OHIO WINTERFEST
TCCCC BEAR 1999

This special little bunny came hidden inside a car-shaped tin and was given to children registered for the annual Springtime in Atlanta TCCCC Convention, held March 30 to April 4, 1999.

Smaller than other collector club bean bags, this cute bunny is made of gray terry cloth fabric with pink ears and feet. A red tee states "Enjoy Coca-Cola" on the front and "Springtime in Atlanta TCCCC 1999" on the back. His amusing smile and huggable size made it hard to get out of the hands of children and into the hands of collectors.

Serious collectors were on the hunt for this collector club edition from the start, and presales on the Internet hit high prices before anyone knew for sure what the bean bag would be. With only two hundred made worldwide, these little bunnies will probably remain collector favorites.

editions, this brown fuzzy bear comes with a "homemade" numbered swing tag that hangs around its neck with a red cord. It was given as a breakfast gift to registrants of the Ohio Winterfest Coca-Cola Convention, held in Zanesville, Ohio, each February.

The brown Winterfest bear wears a red T-shirt that states, "Enjoy Coca-Cola" on the front and "Winterfest TCCCC 1999" on the back. By this point collector club editions had become big business on the secondary market, and the Winterfest bear brought the highest Internet auction price of any collector club edition at more than $400 (possibly because of its numbered tag).

BADGER CHAPTER TCCCC SPRING PAUSE COW 1999

Issued 5/99
Quantity 250
Price Guide: $125–175

Some call it a bull, others call it a cow. Regardless, only two

SPRINGTIME IN ATLANTA BUNNY 1999

hundred and fifty black and white bean bags were produced for the 12th Annual Spring Pause, held in Wisconsin Dells, Wisconsin, May 13-15, 1999, by the Badger Chapter of the TCCCC.

This mini-convention draws enthusiasts and collectors from the Great Lakes region interested in sharing treasures and swapping stories of how they acquired their favorite Coca-Cola collectibles.

Many of the cows came with "dirty faces," because the black paper used to wrap up the registration packets left permanent smudges across their heads. Lying flat, the

SUN N' FUN MILLENNIUM BASH BEAR 1999

cow's red tee states "Enjoy Coca-Cola" on the front and "12th Badger Spring Pause 'Play Refreshed' 1999 TCCCC" on the back.

SUN N' FUN MILLENNIUM BASH BEAR 1999

Issued 6/99 Quantity 297
Price Guide: $125–150

No one pretended these special collector club bean bags were just for children anymore. Flocks of hopeful collectors joined the Florida West Coast Chapter of the TCCCC just to get this special black bear.

On Friday, June 18, 1999, the Sun n' Fun Chapter of the TCCCC held a "Millennium Bash" Mini-convention, drawing avid collectors from across Florida. The exclusive Millennium Black Bear with Red T-shirt features the familiar slogan on front with "Millennium Bash Sun n' Fun TCCCC 1999" on the back.

DALLAS 25th ANNUAL CONVENTION HORSE 1999

Issued 8/99 Quantity 400
Price Guide: $125–150

When the 25th Annual Coca-Cola Collectors Club Convention rolled around in August, bean bag enthusiasts were clamoring for the next exclusive edition. The convention, held in Dallas on August 7-14, was the most-attended event in the history of TCCCC.

DALLAS 25th ANNUAL CONVENTION
HORSE 1999

This brown horse with a furry dark mane and tail has the familiar red tee with "25th Annual Convention TCCCC Dallas, 1999" on the back.

Collectors attending the convention in search of this special edition bean bag were disappointed to find most were distributed at the welcome banquet. Only a few remained to be sold during the swap meet on Saturday.

In the past, various chapters of TCCCC were willing to sell extra bean bags to make a profit for the chapter. The Coca-Cola Collectors Club decided these particular bean bags should only go to members. From that point on, collectors had to depend almost solely on chapter members willing to sell their bean bags.

VIRGINIA BEACH
PARTY DOLPHIN
1999

**VIRGINIA BEACH PARTY
DOLPHIN 1999**

Issued 10/99 Quantity 150
Price Guide: $150–200

The Coca-Cola Collectors Club's Old Dominion Fall Fest, held at Virginia Beach, Virginia, October 13-16, 1999, provided arguably the most unique bean bag thus far. The beach party dolphin is gray and white with blue eyes, and a red foam Coca-Cola life preserver around its middle states, "Enjoy Coca-Cola."

This TCCCC chapter, which draws collectors from the greater D.C. area, holds an annual fall swap meet and mini-convention packed with interesting vintage collectibles and the newest in Coca-Cola collecting every year.

**CHOO-CHOO CHAPTER TCCCC
DALMATIAN 1999**

Issued 11/99 Quantity 160
Price Guide: $175–200

The fifteenth anniversary of the Choo-Choo Chapter "Connection" Convention in Chattanooga, Tennessee, was held November 4-6, 1999, and marked the release of the next anticipated collectors club bean bag.

This black and white Dalmatian sports the red tee as well as "15th Anniversary TCCCC Choo-Choo Chap-

CHOO-CHOO CHAPTER DALMATIAN 1999

**ATLANTA CHAPTER
TCCCC CHRISTMAS
PIG 1999**
*Issued 12/99
Quantity 150
Price Guide: $125–175*

ter 1999" on the back. This is one of the harder collector club editions to find and rarely appears for auction on the Internet.

**NW GEORGIA TCCCC
MERRY CHRISTMAS PARTY CAT 1999**
*Issued 12/99 Quantity 85
Price Guide: $150–200*

The Northwest Georgia Chapter created the Christmas Party Cat to commemorate its tenth annual celebration. This brown cat with white ears and mouth wears the familiar red T-shirt with "Merry Christmas" and "Celebrating 10 Years TCCCC 1999 NW Georgia Chapter" printed on the back.

Like other collector club bean bags, the brown cat lies flat, but response to the toy was anything but. Collectors pestered members of the chapter for news before the cat was released, and it is one of the harder to find as well, since few members have been willing

From the TCCCC chapter that started it all comes this bright pink pig with darker pink snouts and ears and a red scarf that reads, "Enjoy Coca-Cola Atlanta Chapter Christmas 1999 TCCCC." Atlanta members handed out this pig to fellow members at their annual Christmas party. However, a few members got their pig in advance, causing quite a stir

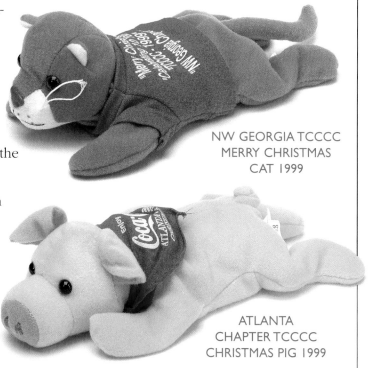

NW GEORGIA TCCCC MERRY CHRISTMAS CAT 1999

ATLANTA CHAPTER TCCCC CHRISTMAS PIG 1999

when the cute swine began appearing on Internet auction sites ahead of time.

OHIO VALLEY CHAPTER TCCCC
19th CHRISTMAS PARTY MONKEY 1999
Issued 12/99 Quantity 72
Price Guide: $150–200

The nineteenth annual Christmas party marked the occasion for the Ohio Valley Chapter of the TCCCC to release its second numbered collector club bean bag. This Christmas Monkey comes with a red tee stating "Ohio Valley 19th Christmas Party 1999 TCCCC."

Only seventy-two monkeys with the long tail and quizzical face were made and distributed to members attending the Cincinnati Christmas party, along with a package of

OHIO VALLEY
CHAPTER
TCCCC
CHRISTMAS
MONKEY 1999

other Coca-Cola favors. The handmade swing tag gives the number of each monkey.

CHOO-CHOO CHAPTER TCCCC
CHRISTMAS PARTY SQUIRREL 1999
Issued 12/99 Quantity 125
Price Guide: $175–250

Another tricky collector club edition to find comes from the Choo-Choo Chapter of the TCCCC. Given out at the chapter's Christmas party in Chattanooga, Tennessee, this squirrel in the red hat is wearing a green shirt with "Enjoy Coca-Cola" on the front and "Choo-Choo Christmas Party 1999 TCCCC" on the back.

This squirrel was originally slated to be given out at the party, but problems in getting permission from Coca-Cola delayed its release until March 2000. Only a handful of the toys have shown up for sale on Internet auction sites, fetching big prices.

CHOO-CHOO TCCCC
CHRISTMAS PARTY SQUIRREL 1999

OHIO WINTERFEST TCCCC MOUSE 2000

Issued 2/2000   Quantity 200
Price Guide: $125–175

This gray mouse has a long pink nose with whiskers and big gray ears with pink insides. It was produced by the Ohio Winterfest TCCCC for its mini-convention in Zanesville, Ohio, February 23-26, 2000. This annual event attracts Coca-Cola collectors from a wide area.

The red tee comes on this mouse as well, with the usual "Enjoy Coca-Cola" on the front and "Ohio Winterfest 2000 TCCCC" on the back. Like many other collector club bean bags, the mouse lies flat.

The Ohio Winterfest committee limited outside sales, so numbers available for purchase by non-members is very low. Collectors like the numbered swing tag on this edition.

What new collector club bean bags might be coming up? It's hard to predict, but annual chapter meetings and mini-conventions may have more special editions in the works. Below is a table of recent and future conventions not covered in this edition.

Many clubs hold Christmas parties, so there's always the potential for a new bean bag.

Refer to Appendix B for more information about the Coca-Cola Collectors Club.

EVENT	LOCATION	DATE
Spring Fling	Independence, Missouri	March, 2000
Springtime in Atlanta	Atlanta, Georgia	April, 2000
Badger Spring Pause	Wisconsin Dells, Wisconsin	May, 2000
Smokeyfest	Gatlinburg, Tennessee	May, 2000
26th Annual Convention	Greensboro, North Carolina	July, 2000
Septemberfest	Elizabethtown, Kentucky	September, 2000
Coca-Cola Days	Atlantic, Iowa	September, 2000
Minnefest	Rochester, Minnesota	October, 2000
Choo-Choo Connection	Chattanooga, Tennessee	November, 2000
Atlanta Christmas Party	Atlanta, Georgia	December, 2000
27th Annual Convention	Orlando, Florida	July, 2001
28th Annual Convention	Palm Springs, California	July, 2002

CHAPTER 11

Coca-Cola Authorized International Editions

"Wherever thirst goes"
— 1942 advertising copy

With the expansion of the secondary market on the Internet, collecting knows no boundaries. A special Coke bean bag that comes out one day in Australia appears the next day on Websites for potential buyers around the world.

Highly prized by collectors in the United States and Canada, Coca-Cola bean bags from other countries represent the most exciting, challenging and uncertain group of collectibles around. But getting reliable information is often difficult.

How do you know what is real and what is fake? How do you find out when and where these rarer editions might be coming out? What's a fair price? Whom can you trust?

The key is to know as much as possible about a potential international edition before you buy. Ask for photos. Check other websites to see if descriptions and photos match the bean bag you are considering buying.

And be sure the seller is ethical. Many auction sites now give ratings for buyers and sellers so you can see what other customers have said. Many Internet sellers don't want the trouble and added expense of cashing checks. Sending cash without registering the letter can be risky.

Always compare prices. With new editions, the price usually drops after the initial flurry of activity on the Internet. Waiting just two weeks can result in getting a bean bag for half the cost. With retired editions, the prices keep climbing as they become rarer. Buy as close to the day of the event or promotion as you can for the lowest price.

The Coca-Cola Company has authorized a limited number of international bean bags, whether they're for promotions involving sales of Coke products, sold at markets and restaurants or used as prizes in games.

Although most international editions closely resemble the familiar old face polar bear, seal and reindeer designs, there are several differences. To distinguish bean bags coming from other countries look for variations in size (many are smaller), clothing and accessories, flat Coca-Cola button logos and, often, poorer quality plush fabric and stitching.

With few exceptions, international editions have no swing tags and no style numbers. Tush tags carry the familiar "Coca-Cola brand plush" registered trademark.

DOWN UNDER EDITIONS

Coca-Cola licensed editions produced in Australia and New Zealand are manufactured by International Merchandising Concepts (IMC). Made in China, many resemble American/Canadian editions made by CGI, but have several important differences. About as many of these popular Coca-Cola bean bags end up in the hands of North American collectors as those down under!

AUSTRALIAN HUNGRY JACK'S
BUDDY BEARS 1997

Polar Bear with Red Bow
Polar Bear with Fed Fringed Scarf
Price Guide: $100 a pair in bags

The first authorized Australian editions came out for a promotion at Hungry Jack's Restaurants in late 1997 (otherwise known as Burger King in New Zealand and the rest of the world). The promotion offered one bear for purchase at $4.95 AU with every hamburger and Coke. "Got your Buddy Bear yet?" signs hung over Hungry Jack's counters for just a few weeks.

The Buddy Bears can be recognized by their smaller size, thinner bodies and shorter, stitched feet. A small, solid black button serves as the eyes on both bears, unlike the brown and black centered eyes of the CGI versions. The girl bear comes with a red ribbon in her hair and flat red Coca-Cola button logo on the left side of her chest. The boy sports a red scarf with black fringe and the "Enjoy Coca-Cola" logo printed on it.

Each white polar bear came in its own sealed bag with a paper insert identifying it as one of the Hungry Jack's Buddy Bears. Original inserts stated Hungry Jack's for the girl and Burger King for the boy. Only a very few boy Buddy Bears ever had Hungry Jack's inserts.

The most distinctive feature is the tush

HUNGRY JACK'S BUDDY BEAR TUSH TAG

tag, with "Enjoy Coca-Cola Buddy Bear." This tush tag has been used on several other editions from Australia.

VILLAGE CINEMA BEARS 1998

Bubbles (boy bear with plaid bowtie)
Fizz (girl bear with plaid bow and button)
Price Guide: Estimate $200–300 a pair

Perhaps the most difficult Coca-Cola bears to find in the world, the Village Cinema Bears, were released for just two weeks in early 1998. With the purchase of a large Coke and popcorn, Village Cinema Theatre goers could purchase one of these rare treasures.

Fizz looks very much like the girl Hungry Jack's polar bear with a red plaid bow in her hair and flat red Coca-Cola button on her chest. Bubbles is a white polar bear with a red plaid bowtie. He does not have the flat red Coca-Cola button on his chest. Both bean bags have tush tags with "Enjoy Coca-Cola Buddy Bear."

Real and fake Village Cinema bears have appeared on the Internet from time to time and are very sought-after by collectors. Since they closely resemble Buddy Bears it is important to know how to identify

AUSTRALIAN HUNGRY JACK'S BUDDY BEARS 1997

NEW ZEALAND BURGER KING BUDDY BEARS 1998

them. The key to recognizing Fizz is that the red Coca-Cola button is on the right side of her chest. Bubbles can be identified by the red plaid bowtie with no ribbon around his neck.

NEW ZEALAND BURGER KING
BUDDY BEARS 1998

Polar Bear with Plaid Ribbon

Polar Bear with Plaid Bowtie

Polar Bear with Red Vest

Polar Bear with Red Scarf

Price Guide $200–300

a set of 4; $50–60 each

Burger King in New Zealand ran a promotion in mid-1998 offering two pairs of Buddy Bears for sale. With the purchase of a combo meal (Coke, hamburger and fries totaling $12 NZ), the customer could choose between four editions of Buddy Bears.

The red set was released first. One polar bear comes dressed in a red fabric vest complete with black knotted buttons and "Enjoy Coca-Cola" printed on it. The other, essentially the same as the Hungry Jack's polar bear, comes with a red scarf with black fringe and "Enjoy Coca-Cola."

The plaid set followed with the girl polar bear wearing a plaid bow in her hair and flat red Coca-Cola button on the left side of her

NEW ZEALAND BURGER KING BUDDY BEARS INSERTS
(RED AND BLACK, RED ONLY)

chest. The boy bear wears a plaid bowtie a with ribbon around his neck. This pair has been mistakenly bought as the more valuable Village Cinema bears because collectors did not know the difference.

Smaller with less stuffing, all bears came in their own sealed bags with paper inserts identifying them as Burger King Buddy Bears. All four have the "Enjoy Coca-Cola Buddy Bear" tush tag. Not as well made as their American counterparts, some came with missing parts. It is not unusual to find one without a tush tag or with a paper insert printed only in red (the black part not printed).

AUSTRALIAN KMART SET OF 4 1998

Seal in Baseball Cap
Penguin in Delivery Cap
Polar Bear in Red Baseball Cap
Polar Bear in Red Shirt
Price Guide $100–120 a set of 4;
$25–30 each

In the summer of 1998, a set of four bean bags, looking remarkably like the first set released in the United States and Canada, appeared in Australian Kmart stores. The set consisted of two polar bears, a penguin, and a seal all with flat bottle cap swing tags. (Cavanagh editions have the same shape but are book style.) None of the tags gave a style number or name.

Some unscrupulous Internet auction sellers have tried to pass these four off as rare "error" or "prototype" bean bags from the first Spring 1997 set (CGI). The Australian Kmart set can be differentiated in the following ways:

- *Seal* — has a red-and-white baseball cap that faces forward, a rounder face and stitched line between the nose and mouth.
- *Penguin* — wears a green delivery cap without a button (like the first edition set) and a smaller red satin bowtie.
- *Polar Bear in Red Shirt* — has a larger

AUSTRALIAN KMART SET OF 4

Coca-Cola Collectible Bean Bags & Plush

face with less stuffing, a slightly larger plastic nose, and stitching between the nose and mouth.

- *Polar Bear in Red Cap* — also has a larger face with less stuffing, a slightly larger plastic nose, and stitching between the nose and mouth.
- Both polar bears are made from a slightly off-white plush fabric.

The Kmart Australian set has many more manufacturing flaws, such as bits of stuffing hanging out, extra threads and incompletely sewn seams. It is very hard to find a set with Mint tags since the beans were dumped into baskets for sale. Some came with shelf hooks on their heads so they could be hung for display. This set also appeared at Woolworths in a few Australian cities in 1998.

SURFACE WASHABLE ONLY
DO NOT MACHINE WASH
ALL NEW MATERIALS
100% POLYESTER
MADE IN CHINA
MANUFACTURED & DISTRIBUTED BY
INTERNATIONAL MERCHANDISING CONC
(613) 9699 6799

AUSTRALIAN
BUNNIES TUSH TAG

The growing number of Australian bean bag collectors, not to mention the insatiable North American collectors, were now ready for many more editions.

CHINESE NEW YEAR/EASTER BUNNIES 1999

Bunny in Red Vest
Bunny in Red Scarf
Bunny in Red Pants
Bunny with Ball
Price Guide: $60–80 a set of 4; $15–20 each

Released for sale in early March of 1999, this unique set of four bunnies celebrated both the Chinese New Year (Year of the Rabbit) and Easter. For one month only, these playful looking bunnies were available at Mobil Gas Station Stores (Quix) in most of Australia.

Most gas station stores sold out of these wildly popular bunnies faster than the allotted month's time. Unequal distribution of all four also left collectors hopping all over major cities in search of a complete set.

AUSTRALIAN CHINESE NEW YEAR/EASTER BUNNIES 1999

Requiring a gas fill-up and purchase of a two-liter bottle of a Coke product, the cost per bunny came to $24 AU (not counting fill-up or tax).

Internet auction sites were flooded with the bunnies for prices less than the basic cost. Many speculated that entrepreneurs who worked at Mobil Gas Stations had taken home large quantities for resale.

AUSTRALIAN CHRISTMAS SET OF 4 1999

Penguin with Red Ribbon
Seal with Red Cap and Red Ribbon
Reindeer with Red Ribbon
Polar Bear with Red Bow and Ribbon
Price Guide: $100–$140 a set; $25–30 each

Christmastime 1999 served as the occasion for four of the cutest Coca-Cola brand bean bag plush critters yet to hit Australian

AUSTRALIAN CHRISTMAS SET OF 4 1999

Each bunny comes with a whimsical smile, large eyes, long playful ears, and huge feet with pink fabric patches. All bunnies have flat red Coca-Cola buttons on the left sides of their chests or outfits. None have swing tags. The tush tag states, "'Enjoy Coca-Cola' advertising authorisation by The Coca-Cola Company" on the front and "Manufactured and Distributed by International Merchandising Concepts" on the back.

BP Petroleum gas stations. The toys, packaged in sealed bags with a red display hanger advertising all four, were only available with purchase of a Coca-Cola product and a fill-up.

Each plush bean bag looks very much like other editions released in North America with several differences. All have flat red Coca-Cola buttons on their chests, and all have tush tags identical to the bunny set.

But differences in body shape and style include:

- *Polar Bear* — has an old face smile with bigger eyes and a different nose.
- *Seal* — has a red fabric hat with black trim.
- *Penguin* — sports oval eyes and a different yellow-orange fabric is used on the beak and feet.

The reindeer is virtually identical to the new editions.

None of the bean bags have swing tags, and the tush tags state, "'Enjoy Coca-Cola' advertising authorisation by The Coca-Cola Company" on the front and "Manufactured and Distributed by International Merchandising Concepts" on the back.

AUSTRALIAN AMF BOWLER BEAR 1999
Price Guide: $25–40 each

AMF Bowler Bears are old face polar bears that come with a flat red Coca-Cola button and an AMF bowling logo on a red scarf. The bear looks remarkably like the first male Buddy Bear but with a swing tag and less stuffing than other editions. The tush tag is of the regular International Merchandising Concepts variety.

The bear, available only from AMF Ten Pin Bowling Centers in Queensland, Australia, could only be purchased when you bowled a game and bought a Coke. Most of the Ten Pin Bowling Centers sold out in a matter of days — about how long it took collectors to find out about this fuzzy little guy.

Internet sales of international editions such as the AMF Bowler Bear make for booming business that will only get bigger as the world shrinks and hobbyists expand their collections to include international versions.

AUSTRALIAN AMF BOWLER BEAR 1999

AUSTRALIAN FOOTBALL LEAGUE BEARS 2000
Adelaide Crows

Brisbane Lions

Carlton Blues

Collingwood Magpies

Essendon Bombers

Footscray Bulldogs

Fremantle Dockers

Geelong Cats

Hawthorn Hawks

Melbourne Demons

North Melbourne Kangaroos

Port Adelaide Port Power

ADELAIDE CROWS BEAR FROM THE
AUSTRALIAN FOOTBALL LEAGUE BEARS 2000

Richmond Tigers

Saint Kilda Saints

Sydney Swans

West Coast Eagles

Price Guide $240–320 a set;

$20–25 individually

In the biggest release of bean bags out-side the United States, the Australian Football League (AFL) produced sixteen different team polar bears for their 2000 season. Each bear comes dressed in its respective team's colors and a team logo scarf. Each has a Fan Zone swing tag and Coca-Cola logo tush tag. The bears are made by Hunter Leisure in China.

Getting all sixteen of these sporting little bears is quite a challenge since each is avail-able only from the individual team's Fan Zone Merchandise center located across Australia. Internet sites boomed when the first Lions

RICHMOND TIGERS BEAR FROM THE
AUSTRALIAN FOOTBALL LEAGUE BEARS 2000

AFL bear appeared for auction. No sooner had collectors bought one edition, than another popped up. Everyone wondered how many would be issued.

EUROPEAN EDITIONS

Licensed Coca-Cola editions produced for European consumers are connected with promotions to sell company beverage prod-ucts, sometimes at restaurant chains and sometimes as redemption prizes for winning a Coke game. None of the editions are made by CGI, so none have bottle cap swing tags with style numbers.

ENGLISH COCA-COLA CAN 1998
Price Guide: $50–60 each

A U.S. company with European affiliates, Play-by-Play (also located in Spain) provided its own interesting twist on the bean bag

Australian Football

- **ADELAIDE CROWS**

- **BRISBANE LIONS**

- **CARLTON BLUES**

- **COLLINGWOOD MAGPIES**

- **ESSENDON BOMBERS (NOT SHOWN)**

- **FOOTSCRAY WESTERN BULLDOGS (NOT SHOWN)**

- **FREMANTLE DOCKERS (NOT SHOWN)**

- **GEELONG CATS**

League Bears 2000

- **HAWTHORN HAWKS**

- **MELBOURNE DEMONS**

- **N. MELBOURNE KANGAROOS**

- **PORT ADELAIDE PORT POWER**

- **RICHMOND TIGERS**

- **SAINT KILDA SAINTS (NOT SHOWN)**

- **SYDNEY SWANS**

- **WEST COAST EAGLES**

ENGLISH COCA-COLA CAN

market in 1998. This bean bag is a can of "Coca-Cola classic" standing eight inches tall and made of shiny fabric and lots of beans. Silver top and bottom caps sewn on the red Coke can are designed to look just like the new release of "Coca-Cola classic" in Europe.

It carries a rectangular swing tag with the familiar icy Coca-Cola Red Disc icon. Some editions did not come with swing tags at all. The tush tag is the standard Play-by-Play authorized tag.

This Coke can bean bag was available at toy stores in Britain but didn't get much attention from collectors until a

couple appeared for auction in 2000 on the Internet. It is one of the rarer editions of European Coca-Cola bean bags.

GERMAN POLAR BEAR IN COKE CAN 1998
Price Guide: $150–175 each

This cute little white polar bear from Germany is part of the advertising campaign launched in the summer of 1998 to announce the return of the North Pole polar bear advertisements.

Much smaller than other polar bears released in both the United States and internationally, it has the unique distinction of coming in a special Coke can. The can, printed in German, states, "Der Coca-Cola Polar Bar aus der Dose (the Coca-Cola polar bear in the can)" with a picture of a baby polar bear drinking a bottle of Coke.

GERMAN BEAR IN COKE CAN 1998

GERMAN BEAR IN COKE CAN 1999

GERMAN BEAR
IN COKE CAN
TUSH TAG

Two thousand of the cans were supposed to be produced, but reported problems limited supplies to less than sixteen hundred. His tiny size and more squishable stuffing allows this little bear to fit perfectly into his steel can.

The bottle of Coca-Cola in his right paw, featuring a red label printed in English on one side and German on the other, is much larger than other editions. The tush tag is printed in German. The bear is reported to have been made in Indonesia by PM GMBH Berlin/Germany, although the tush tag does not specify.

GERMAN BEAR IN COKE CAN 1999
Price Guide: $125–150 each

The second polar bear in a Coke can from Germany arrived late in 1999 as part of a promotion to sell Coke products connected to Burger King restaurants. Some were sold with a meal but most required the customer to redeem a winning game piece.

Like the first little bear, this toy comes in a steel Coke can printed in German ("Der Coca-Cola Polar Bar aus der Dose") with a picture of a mother polar bear and cub drinking "the real thing."

This second edition comes dressed in a red felt stocking cap and red Coca-Cola logo scarf with "Coca-Cola Schutzmarke koffein-haltig" printed on the front. The large bottle of Coke is also printed in English and German on a red label.

Production for this little guy is reported to be less than two thousand as well. The tush tag does identify PM GMBH Berlin/Germany as the distributor.

GERMAN TRINK POLAR BEAR 1999
Price Guide: $75–125 each

A "Christmas in July" promotion offered a special white Coca-Cola polar bear as a prize for lucky consumers who found winning caps on two-liter bottles of Coke products. An estimated two thousand bears were

GERMAN TRINK BEAR 1999

GERMAN PENGUIN PRIZE 1999

Price Guide: $200–300 each

Released only in the North Rhine river region, this cuddly penguin was offered as a prize to lucky consumers who found the winning game piece under the cap of a two-liter bottle of Coke. Some sources say just fifty of the penguins were made for the game.

produced, but how many got into winners' hands is only a guess.

People quickly called this bear the "Trink (Drink) Polar Bear" because of the large red "Trink Coca-Cola Koffeinhaltig" tush tag.

Everything is different about this polar bear. The body shape is bigger and the face is longer with a flat nose completely hiding the stitched smile and tiny pinned-back ears. This rare edition comes with a red-and-white-striped scarf fringed with green yarn and leather inserts on the feet.

Made in Indonesia by Hogberg International, even the bottle of Coca-Cola is shaped differently with smaller lettering. A white card swing tag states in English, "This is not a part of toys. Please remove it (sic) this before giving this toy to a child."

GERMAN
PENGUIN
PRIZE
1999

This lovable penguin comes with a Christmas scarf, much like the red-and-white-striped scarf with green yarn fringe on the Trink Polar Bear. His red cap is embroidered with "Enjoy Coca-Cola." His right paw holds a bottle of Coca-Cola, shaped differently like the Trink version.

The face is smaller than CGI versions and has oval eyes. (Cavanagh versions have flat-bottomed eyes.) A red round Coca-Cola button adorns the left side of his chest. A white swing tag has the same grammatical error as the Trink Polar Bear. The tush tag identifies Hogberg International as the manufacturer; made in Indonesia.

Only twice have these rare penguins appeared on Internet auction sites. Eager collectors have struggled finding these treasures anywhere in the world. Recently, a search turned up only one website that offered these rare penguins for sale.

As an indication of how hard it is to keep up with all the international editions that may be produced for a local promotion halfway around the world, consider this: Rumors of a set of five to be released in the summer of 1999 in Germany surfaced on one website. The set consisted of two polar bears, a seal, penguin and a moose or reindeer. Most probably made by Hogberg International, it was to have come with the same white hang tags and red tush tags as previous German editions. Reli-

able sources in Germany cannot confirm any more information about this set.

ENGLISH MICKEY MOUSE 1999
Price Guide: $75–125 each

In a totally different kind of promotion, Coca-Cola and the Disney Store teamed up for a special game in Britain. Packs of Coca-Cola contained special tokens that could be redeemed for various Disney prizes.

The promotion, "Bring the Good Times Home," offered Mickey bean bags, Mickey and Donald shirts, Mickey clocks and pens. The redemption certificate offered one lucky winner a trip to Walt Disney World Resort in

ENGLISH MICKEY MOUSE 1999

ENGLISH MICKEY MOUSE
ADVERTISEMENT 1999

Collectors were required to collect a specified number of bottle caps to redeem this fuzzy bear. It meant drinking a lot of Coke to redeem this one.

The bear, which comes with a red scarf, a large bottle of Coke in the left paw and black inserts on the feet, is shaped differently than any previous polar bear authorized by Coca-Cola. The most distinguishing feature is its large face with endearing black eyes, little pinned-back ears, and wide smile.

The tush tag indicates it was made by Cyrk Europe under the authority of The Coca-Cola Company. This rare edition has never shown up on lists of authorized Coca-Cola bean bags and has appeared only once or twice on Internet auctions.

Florida for fifteen people by answering some questions and writing a fifteen-word essay.

The special Mickey Mouse bean bags available only through this game do not contain Coca-Cola trademarks. Mickey, standing at more than eight inches, is a delight for Disney, Coca-Cola — or just plain bean bag — collectors.

ENGLISH POLAR BEAR 1999

Price Guide: Estimate $75–100

A large eight-inch polar bear was given away in a promotion in England.

ENGLISH
POLAR BEAR
1999

GERMAN SET OF 8 2000

ENGLISH BURGER KING POLAR BEAR 1999

Price Guide $25–50

In 1999, Burger King restaurants in England ran a special promotion that included a free toy with purchase of a child's meal. The white Coca-Cola polar bear is shaped differently than other editions with a longer triangular face more like the plush polar bear shape. Its tiny ears are farther back on the head, but it has the great smile of Coca-Cola polar bears. This little guy carries a bottle of Coke in his left paw, stitched like the new face bears. The bear has no swing tag but does come with a Coca-Cola authorized tush tag.

Very few of these special little English bears have shown up for sale. Some English collectors have posted photos on their web-sites, and occasionally one appears on Internet auctions. But this bear remains scarce.

GERMAN SET OF 8 2000

Polar Bear with Scarf
Polar Bear with Bowtie
Polar Bear with Bottle
Penguin with Chef's Hat
Penguin with Scarf
Seal with Scarf
Seal with Life Preserver
Polar Bear with Red Scarf
*Price Guide: $250–300 a complete set;
$30–40 individual*

A new German set of eight Coca-Cola bean bags appeared in February of 2000 and disappeared very quickly. Each toy comes with a distinctive round swing tag in a bottle

Coca-Cola Collectible Bean Bags & Plush   133

HONG KONG FAMILY OF BEARS 1999

cap design by Play-by-Play Company of England and Spain. Tush tags printed in German carry the Coca-Cola logo. The bottle of Coke this set holds is much larger than other versions.

Many avid bean bag collectors in Germany missed this set entirely because it arrived unexpectedly in toy stores and rapidly disappeared. Appearing only a handful of times on Internet auctions, this has become one of the most difficult international sets to complete. Individual members of the set first sold for $15-20 until anxious bidders realized there were eight different bean bags available. Prices rose dramatically when the last editions were put up for auction.

HONG KONG EDITIONS
HONG KONG FAMILY OF BEARS 1999

PaPa Bear (Large with pipe and red scarf)
MaMa Bear (Large with green scarf)
LaLa Bear (Small with red cap and shirt)
CoCo Bear (Small with green shirt and shades)
Price Guide: $200–400 for set;
$50–75 each; CoCo $100–125 each

A family of four Coca-Cola Polar Bears arrived in April of 1999 as part of a promotion to sell Coca-Cola in Hong Kong. With the purchase of specially packaged two 1.25-liter bottles of any Coke product, one bean bag member of the family came attached. Only MSRP stores of Hong Kong featured this offer.

Giant posters advertised the family of bears. PaPa Bear and MaMa Bear are larger at seven inches high, while LaLa Bear and CoCo Bear are slightly less than six inches tall.

PaPa Bear comes with a red scarf wrapped around his neck, a brown pipe in his left paw and a bottle of Coke in his right paw. The eyes are the same size as other bean bags, but the nose is larger.

MaMa Bear is dressed in a green scarf embroidered with flowers at the ends. She holds a bottle of Coke in her right paw, and like PaPa, her eyes are the same size with her nose slightly larger.

LaLa comes with a red baseball cap and red vest embroidered with "Coca-Cola" on the front. Smaller than her parents, she has a different kind of nose, more like that found on seals. A bottle of Coke rests in her right paw.

CoCo is by far the most popular member of the family. This edition, complete with dark glasses and a headset, flew out of stores in one day making it very difficult for collectors to find complete sets. CoCo's green vest is embroidered with "Coca-Cola" on the

front. He holds a bottle of Coke is in his right paw as he rocks out to the music.

Collectors worldwide snatched up every set they could find on the Internet. Because of the difficulty in finding all four, the value of this set has skyrocketed in recent months.

HONG KONG PAIR OF BEARS 1999

Polar Bear in Snowflake Scarf
    and Long Cap
Polar Bear with Crate of Coke
Price Guide: not priced because of questionable authenticity

Collectors are very cautious of editions coming out of Hong Kong because of the high probability they are not authorized Coca-Cola versions. Lots of knock-offs and third shift bean bags come out of China. International trademarks are duplicated without authorization to produce a wide variety of popular products for a fraction of the cost.

The only way to be sure the bean bag is "real" is to check its source. Does the bean bag in question have a tush tag

HONG KONG BEAR
IN SNOWFLAKE SCARF AND CAP 1999

NEW MATERIAL
REG. NO   23t42
CONTENTS
POLYETHYLENE BEADS
POLYESTER FIBER

MATERIAUX NEUFS SEULEME
7   NO.DE PERM
CONTENU
ILLIE DE POLYÉTHYLÈNE
IBRES DE POLYESTER

TUSH TAG:
NOWHERE DOES
IT MENTION
COCA-COLA, GIVE
A MANUFACTURER
OR IDENTIFY THE
SOURCE

with the Coca-Cola trademark? More importantly, did The Coca-Cola Company authorize the promotion? Are there promotional materials (signs, brochures, game rules) showing Coca-Cola authorization? Is the seller willing to provide information on the source of the suspected bean bag?

The next two pairs of bean bags coming out of Hong Kong proves the point well. Both pairs give reason to question their authenticity.

HONG KONG BEAR WITH CRATE 1999

The Polar Bear in Snowflake Scarf and Long Cap was part of a store promotion stating, "Buy two bottles of any Coke product and get a bean bag bear free." Advertisements show the bear with bottles of Coke.

This bear looks remarkably like the World of Coca-Cola exclusive old face #0159 Polar Bear in Red Coca-Cola Snowflake Scarf. The scarf and stocking cap are identical material. The Coke bottle in his right paw is also identical. This fuzzy polar bear has less stuffing than the #0159, different eyes (solid black), and a different kind of nose. All bears came sealed in a plastic bag.

Even though it came from a store promotion in which Coca-Cola products were sold, there is good reason to wonder if this was an authorized production. The questionable part is the toy's tush tag. Printed in English and French, nowhere does it mention Coca-Cola, give a manufacturer or identify the source.

Appearing at the same time on the Internet, a second polar bear looks entirely different. Some viewing a picture of this slightly larger bear have called it a "monkey." The longer flat face, ears placed farther back on the head, triangular nose, and solid eyes don't resemble other polar bears.

The crate of Coke bottles he carries also is suspect. Bottles are amber in color with gold caps and are not the trademarked contour shape. The tush tag identifies Great American Fun Corp. of Columbus, Ohio, as the manufacturer. Nowhere on this bean bag are there any authorized Coca-Cola markings.

Repeated requests for documentation and further information about this questionable bear have been ignored by Internet sellers. Collectors continue to be wary.

HONG KONG PAIR OF SEALS

Seal with Red Scarf and Cap

Seal with Green Vest and Cap

Price Guide: not priced because of question-able authenticity

If the two polar bears are suspect because of their tush tags, the next pair of seals with standard CGI tags are suspect for another reason. Cavanagh Group International does not sell Coca-Cola brand bean bag plush in Hong Kong! Identical to Cavanagh versions of seals produced throughout the years, these two charming little seals have the same familiar shape, face and bottle of Coke.

Obviously made at the same plant as regular CGI editions, the first seal wears a long red scarf with the Coca-Cola logo at the ends. His little red cap with white pompon is a different style than seen before. The other seal has a vest made of fabric identical to that of the Media Play Exclusive set produced in 1998. He also has a little red cap.

The tush tag gives us a clue that these are third shift editions. The date printed is 1997, but this fabric only came out in 1998. Since no additional information has surfaced about these seals, they remain suspect.

HONG KONG SEALS TUSH TAG

HONG KONG PAIR OF SEALS

CHAPTER 12

Miscellaneous Authorized Editions

"Coke is it!"
— 1982 slogan

Collectors are always on the lookout for unusual bean bags, especially ones that are produced for special events. These limited editions, authorized by The Coca-Cola Company, are some of the most collectible around. Here is a sampling of some special editions that are hard to find.

KENTUCKY
WILDCATS 1998

SPORTING EVENTS BEAN BAGS

KENTUCKY WILDCATS BEAN BAG 1999

Price Guide: $100–200

In celebration of the University of Kentucky Wildcats basketball team winning the NCAA Championship in 1998, Coca-Cola released a special Wildcat bean bag. This bright blue plush Wildcat is wearing a Coca-Cola "Always" logo white T-shirt.

Finding this special bean bag is a real challenge. It came in a sealed can hidden in twelve-packs of "Coca-Cola classic" only in the area around the university. Available only for a short while, very few of these Wildcats exist today because collectors only found out about them long after they were gone.

BRUTUS BUCKEYE
IN SEALED COKE CAN 1999

Price Guide: $100–200

"Wherever there's a Buckeye[1], there's Always Coca-Cola!" Ohio State Buckeye fans were treated to a different kind of promotion in late fall of 1999. For a limited time, a special "Always Refreshing Buckeye Fans" Coke can could

be found hidden in regular twelve-packs. Lucky winners received a specially marked, vacuum-sealed can with a surprise inside.

Produced by Vend-a-Win, the Columbus area promotion offered game prizes that included free Coke, tickets to games, and other coupons, in addition to the Buckeye bean bag.

Because of the rich tradition of Ohio State Buckeye athletics, these Brutus Buckeye mascots didn't last long. The exact number of cans distributed is unknown, but

BRUTUS
BUCKEYE

---

[1]The term "Buckeye" refers to a tree related to the horse chestnut with mahogany-colored seeds the size of olives. It has become a nickname for the people of Ohio and was adopted by Ohio State University as its mascot, named "Brutus."

collectors raced from store to store trying to find all the special cans.

MINI COLLECTIBLE EDITIONS

Produced by CGI, these mini collectible editions come with a familiar bottle cap swing tag. The addition of the word "mini" and the larger style script are the only difference from the familiar silver and red tags.

MINI COLLECTIBLE SWING TAG

MINI POLAR BEAR WITH WATCH #205 1999
Price Guide: $20–25

Produced by Cavanagh, these Mini Polar Bears come packaged with a Coca-Cola watch. Not distributed through normal channels, they were marketed in the United States only at a chain store and through a retail catalog for the holiday season.

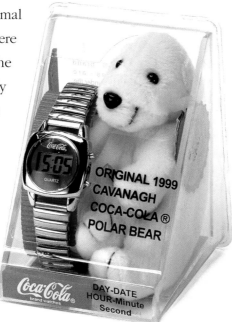

MINI POLAR BEAR WITH WATCH

These fuzzy little bears have a Cavanagh Mini Collectible swing tag with the style number #0205. There is something very compelling about their four-inch size. Faces, with black button eyes and nose, are tiny. A warm stitched smile and mini bottle of Coke makes them hard to resist.

The very same watches also were marketed with a larger plush polar bear. This edition has the plush swing tag and is filled with polyester stuffing — no pellets. It is not a bean bag.

EAT'N PARK RESTAURANT
#213 MINI PENGUIN 1999
Price Guide: $15–25

To celebrate their fiftieth anniversary, Eat'n Park Restaurants wanted to do something special. What originally started as a carhop diner has developed into a chain of seventy restaurants located in Pennsylvania, Ohio and West Virginia. A giant happy face serves as the chain's logo, and "the place for smiles" as its motto. Cavanagh created a new mini penguin for the celebration that began in December, 1999.

This adorable little guy, a smaller version of the familiar penguin, comes with a red Eat'n Park smile logo, cap and red bowtie. The bottle of Coca-Cola in his right paw is about two-thirds the size of regular edition bottles. His face is almost

RUSS BERRIE COCA-COLA EXCLUSIVE

POLAR BEAR 2000

Price Guide: $20–35

Definitely one of the most unusual polar bear bean bags comes from Russ, the famous stuffed toy company. This polar bear has a very lifelike ceramic head, paws and feet with a fuzzy plush body (the bottom is filled with beans, the rest with polyester stuffing). Flexible arms bend in and out so this bear can drink his large acrylic bottle of Coke. With a jaunty red satin scarf, this is an exceptional bear. His seven-inch size is perfect for your desk, table or countertop.

This Russ polar bear is the first in a new series by Russ Berrie designers. However, it will not be available through normal Russ retail stores. Only authorized Coca-Cola outlets will have this special bear available.

the same size as the swing tag. The standard CGI tush tag covers most of his little bottom. He comes sealed in a plastic bag along with the usual warnings.

These endearing little charmers are sure to mark the beginning of a very popular line of mini collectible bean bags for CGI.

RUSS BERRIE
POLAR BEAR
2000

CHAPTER 13

Where To Find Coca-Cola Bean Bags

"Coke follows thirst everywhere"
—1952 advertising copy

Cavanagh Group International has developed many markets for its products. The most well-known is the mass market: national and regional retail chain stores such as Sears, Target, Eckerd Drugs, Kroger, Lowe's, Walgreens, Toys "R" Us, Supervalu, Wards, Michaels, and KB Toys.

There are many independent dealers as well. Some Hallmark stores, drug stores, gift and collectible retailers stock a limited number of current editions of the Coca-Cola brand bean bag plush. Most only have bean bags available for sale during the Christmas season.

In 1998, Cavanagh introduced the Coca-Cola brand Heritage Collection to be sold only through gift stores, Christmas shops and specialty retail outlets. It was created in response to the demand for more upscale collectible products that mass retailers could not handle year-round.

One of the more exciting markets for Coca-Cola brand bean bag plush is the exclusive or specialty market. Special bean bags are made exclusively for a chain of stores, restaurants, special promotions or a cooperative buying group of retailers. These can be the hardest to find and the most valuable.

The most exclusive bean bags have been produced for The World of Coca-Cola. Sold only at the company's Everything Coca-Cola stores, these special editions are treasured by collectors. Several special events have been held at The World of Coca-Cola sites with an exclusive bean bag available only that day.

The secondary market has developed for collectibles that are retired, extremely hard to find or no longer in production. Since popular editions are snapped up the minute they hit the retail shelves, collectors are forced to look elsewhere.

Gift and collectible stores are good sources for older and rarer editions. Stores that specialize in Coca-Cola brand bean bag plush may be able to direct you to secondary market sources in your area.

Trade shows, classified ads, collector magazines and swap meets are other great sources. Coca-Cola collector meetings and

conventions are another place to increase your collection.

One of the most popular sources is the Internet, where you can access collectibles worldwide without leaving your home. Sites may offer information and photos, provide bean bag plush animals available for sale, or direct you to secondary market dealers who specialize in buying, selling and trading.

But Internet auction sites are a gamble. Starting low, prices may look enticing, but they can end up way over their market value when frenzied bidders get caught up in the action. Don't forget to add the costs of shipping to the final amount. Buying individual bean bags at auctions can end up being more expensive than getting an entire set from a store.

Be sure the bean bag and plush toys you are buying are clean with Mint tags. Serious

collectors insist on bean bags that have been stored in a plastic bag or box with a tag protector. They prefer smoke-free and perfume-free environments.

What do you do if your big bargain comes with a spot or damaged tag? Remember that not every Internet auction seller is reliable, so check ratings on auction sites that allow buyers and seller to leave feedback on how transactions worked out. Look for sellers with high ratings indicating they are reliable.

If you are uncertain, email the seller your questions before entering a bid. Remember that bidding on Internet auctions constitutes a legally binding agreement to purchase for the price you have bid. Always ask for insurance on packages being sent to you in case

something is damaged in shipping. It might cost a little more but can be very valuable when that expensive new purchase arrives in pieces.

Counterfeit Coca-Cola brand bean bag plush toys do exist. It is important to purchase your collection from reputable sources. And know what you are buying. Is the bear's striped scarf supposed to have a Coca-Cola logo on it? Do the swing and tush tag match the item correctly?

Members of the Cavanagh Coca-Cola Christmas Society receive a publication every year listing the items available and the retail stores by state that carry their products. (See Chapter 7 and Appendix B for more information about the CCCC Society.)

CHAPTER 14

Collectible Coca-Cola Plush

"Have a Coke and a smile"
— 1979 slogan

It would be easy to fill several books with information just about all of the plush animals bearing the Coca-Cola name through the years, from polar bears of varying colors and sizes, to elephants with life preservers, to hairy gorillas, to penguins and seals . . .

These soft and cuddly plush editions come in all shapes and sizes. Plush toys can be very talented, playing Coke jingles, riding tricycles, serving as puppets, even dancing to music. Others are just so cute they don't need gimmicks to earn a collector's interest.

What makes them plush is their stuffing material and fuzzy

plush fabrics. No beans! (Although, many mini-plush have larger matching plush editions.) What makes them collectible is their Coca-Cola brand name, adorable design and growing popularity.

Many companies have produced authorized Coca-Cola plush toys, including stuffed toy manufacturers Play-by-Play and Dakin and motion toy maker TrendMasters, Inc. Several lines of plush stand out from the rest as being the most collectible.

"ALWAYS" BEAR
SWING TAG FRONT

Since 1993, Cavanagh Group International has produced some of the hottest new designs yearly, creating a growing demand by collectors and children alike.

"THE BEAR EVERYONE IS THIRSTING AFTER!"

Who can resist the famous North Pole polar bear, star of his own television advertisement series? Produced in sizes ranging from a small six inches to giant thirty-inch versions, the floppy white bear comes with a big smile on his face and a big bottle of Coca-Cola in his paw ready to be your friend.

The "Always" editions come with Coca-Cola bottle patches on their chests. A special valentine's edition featured a heart on the bear's T-shirt. One polar bear even came in his own vinyl can of Coke. So whether you are a serious bear collector, or just like

the way they look, their appeal is obvious.

All plush produced by CGI comes with a large swing tag picturing the "Always" bear as well as the statement, "You've seen him on TV delighting fans in millions of dens across the country. Now the lovable Coca-Cola Polar Bear is here with his polar buddies to warm the home of any family they join." Plush editions are not numbered.

Just as new face bean bag bears were introduced in 1999, new face plush polar bears also arrived on the scene wearing a variety

EVERYTHING COCA-COLA NEW YORK
5th AVE. PLUSH POLAR BEAR "NEW FACE"

THREE BURGER KING PLUSH BEARS

of colorful outfits. Dressed in soda fountain jerk outfits, snowflake stocking caps and scarves, vests and hats, these bears are designed to make you smile.

Like their smaller bean bag cousins, plush polar bears also can be made exclusively for one chain of stores. When the #0113 Polar Bear in Long Snowflake Cap debuted in 1997, a larger plush edition was released exclusive to Musicland stores. Other exclusive plush polar bears have been issued for Media Play stores in other years as well.

Everything Coca-Cola Stores also carry exclusive plush polar bears in various sizes. Growing in popularity with collectors, these editions feature a tee shirt with the store's logo and

name. With the closing of the New York 5th Avenue store, the only editions now available are from Atlanta and Las Vegas.

A few authorized editions also were released overseas in various Coca-Cola promotions. Here is a sampling:

In Thailand in 1999, a set of three plush polar bears was issued for Burger King restaurants. Each of the cuddly bears, stand-

SINGAPORE MILLENNIUM BEARS

ing seven inches tall, wears an accessory with a Coca-Cola logo and Burger King logo on it. One wears a red T-shirt. Another sports a red scarf with white fringe. And the last wears a red knit cap. All three came in sealed Burger King bags, and none carry Coke bottles or tags. It is very difficult to find all three.

To celebrate the new millennium, Singapore issued a rare pair of 2000 plush polar bears holding red hearts. This grinning 2000 pair is dressed up to celebrate with formal bow tie and hair ribbon. Each carries a large bottle of Coke. The red satin heart is decorated with confetti and states, "Enjoy Coca-Cola 2000 Celebrate Refreshment." Both come with red rectangular swing tags printed in Chinese.

PLUSH ORNAMENT SWING TAG

PLUSH ORNAMENTS

Looking much like their bean bag cousins, Coca-Cola plush ornaments are fast becoming a Christmas tradition. Cavanagh released these attractive plush ornaments, featuring animals decked out for the holidays, starting in 1995. Prices generally are in the $5-6 range.

Starting in 1998, plush ornaments have been issued for only one Christmas and then retired, making them more collectible. All carry a diamond-shaped swing tag without a style number.

SODA FOUNTAIN BEARS

Created to represent a playful look at Coca-Cola history, Dr. John S. Pembearton

SAMPLING OF PLUSH ORNAMENTS

Name	Issued	Retired
Polar Bear w/Red Earmuffs	1995	1997
Polar Bear w/Bow Tie	1995	1997
Polar Bear w/Red Santa Hat	1995	1997
Polar Bear w/Package & Coke	1995	1997
Stand-up Polar Bear w/Red Earmuffs	1996	1997
Stand-up Polar Bear w/Bowtie	1996	1997
Stand-up Polar Bear w/Red Santa Hat	1996	1997
Stand-up Polar Bear w/Package	1996	1997
Polar Bear w/Stocking & Coke	1997	1997
Stand-up Polar Bear w/Red Vest	1997	1997
Polar Bear w/Skates	1997	1998
Polar Bear w/Red Tee Shirt	1997	1997
Stand-up Polar Bear in Stocking	1997	1998
Stand-up Penguin & Coke	1997	1997
Reindeer in Scarf & Hat	1998	1998
Walrus in Red Coca-Cola Scarf	1998	1998
Penguin in Long Snowflake Hat	1998	1998
Seal in Red Coca-Cola Scarf & Hat	1998	1998
Walrus w/Cap & Red Scarf	1999	1999
Seal w/Red Coca-Cola Sweater	1999	1999
Polar Bear w/Hat & Star	1999	1999
Reindeer in Green Sweater	1999	1999
Penguin w/Red Bow & Candy Cane	1999	1999
Polar Bear w/Red Bow & Gift	1999	1999

owns a pharmacy and soda shoppe in old Atlanta. Soda jerks and patrons all congregate at his establishment to enjoy the sparkling drink: Coca-Cola, in vintage glasses. Even calendar girl, Lillian Bearica, in her floral print dress, stops by for a visit with her friend, Bearry Bearresford, extraordinary soda jerk.

Definitely for serious collections, the high-end Soda Fountain Bears are available only at selected Heritage Dealers. Each bear has finely detailed vintage clothing, a certifi-

DR. PEMBEARTON
AND LILLIAN
BEARICA
SODA FOUNTAIN
BEARS

SODA FOUNTAIN BEARS

Name	Description	Number	Issued	Price
Dr. Pembearton	tan and brown suit	HH0201	1998	$60-65
Lillian Bearica	straw hat and pink dress	HH0202	1998	$70-75
Bearry Bearresford	soda jerk	HH0203	1998	$50-55
Bearnice Bearringer	red dress	HH0204	1998	$60-65
Cubby Bearringer	green suit	HH0205	1998	$60-65
Tessie Bear	blue dress	HH0206	1998	$60-65
George Bearton	soda jerk	HH0210	1999	$60-65
Zoltan Bearrenzinski	policeman	HH0211	1999	$70-75
Bearnard Bearansson	delivery man	HH0212	1999	$60-65
Frau Bruinhilda Bearlinger	green dress and hat	HH0213	1999	$60-65
QVC Exclusive 100 Years Bear	brown bear with logo	HH0216	1999	$50-55
Umbearto Cappy Diaz	blue jump suit with apron	HH0220	2000	$50-55
Herbeart Smartenuff	boy bear in nickers	HH0221	2000	$60-65

cate of authenticity and the Coca-Cola trademark stitched on its right foot.

To date, thirteen Soda Fountain Bears have been released (one exclusively for QVC commemorating the hundredth anniversary of the Chattanooga Coca-Cola Bottling Plant). None have yet retired, although rumor has it that these highly desirable collector bears will start retiring soon.

"POLAR BEAR" BY STEIFF 1999
Price Guide: $350–400

Topping the list of Coca-Cola brand plush is the unique — and expensive — Steiff Polar Bear. Steiff, one of the finest makers of collectible plush bears in the world, created an heirloom Coca-Cola polar bear for its exclusive collection.

Limited to ten thousand, this bear is covered in mohair with jointed arms, airbrushed facial features, suede paws, and knit scarf. Holding a bottle of Coke, this bear sports a red enamel Coca-Cola icon on its chest and a distinctive numbered tag in its ear. Surprisingly solid, this is not a floppy plush bear. The Steiff bear "sits" more than fifteen inches high.

FAO SCHWARZ POLAR BEAR
Price Guide: $475

FAO Schwarz offers the largest polar bear around (stuffed that is) that is not only enormous at four feet tall, but also the most hug-

gable edition ever made. This giant bear is made of the softest plush with trademark Coca-Cola new face eyes and sculpted black nose. With stitched paws and feet, children can literally lose themselves in the arms of this polar bear classic.

SMALL PLUSH

A new size of plush, called "Small Plush" also is scheduled for a 2000 debut.

These little stuffed animals are about the same size as bean bags, but go without beans or bottle cap swing tags.

The set of six features a polar bear in a red soda fountain outfit; a reindeer in a green-striped jacket; a polar bear with a red stocking cap and a green "Happy Holidays" scarf; a penguin in a red vest and soda cap; a polar bear in a red delivery outfit; and a penguin with snowflake cap and "Seasons Greetings" scarf.

The traditional "Large Plush" for 2000 will feature the same styles as the "Small Plush."

2000 PLUSH, POLAR BEAR SODA JERK

List of All Coca-Cola Bean Bags

(SETS LISTED IN CHRONOLOGICAL ORDER)

WINTER 1997 SET

❑ #0101 Seal in Scarf (red striped)

❑ #0102 Seal in Snowflake Cap

❑ #0103 Penguin in Stocking Cap

❑ #0104 Polar Bear in Snowflake Cap

❑ #0105 Polar Bear in Plaid Ribbon

❑ #0106 Polar Bear in Red Bow

SPRING 1997 SET

❑ #0107 Seal in Baseball Cap

❑ #0108 Penguin with Delivery Cap

❑ #0109 Polar Bear with Bottle

❑ #0110 Polar Bear in Pink Bow

❑ #0111 Polar Bear in Baseball Cap

❑ #0112 Polar Bear in Tee Shirt

MUSICLAND/MEDIA PLAY EXCLUSIVE 1997

❑ #0113 Polar Bear in Long Snowflake Cap

SPRING (HERITAGE) EVERYDAY 1998

❑ #0114 Seal in Ski Cap

❑ #0116 Polar Bear in Sweater

❑ #0124 Walrus with Coca-Cola Bottle & Logo Scarf

❑ #0132 Coca-Cola Can in Shades

❑ #0133 Reindeer in Shirt

❑ #0140 Polar Bear in Drivers Cap and Bowtie

WINTER (MASS) 1998 SET

❑ #0118 Polar Bear in Snowflake Hat

❑ #0120 Polar Bear in Red Scarf

❑ #0123 Seal in Green Scarf

❑ #0141 Walrus in Coca-Cola Snowflake Night Cap

❑ #0142 Reindeer in Coca-Cola Snowflake Scarf

❑ #0155 Penguin in Coca-Cola Snowflake Scarf

CCCC SOCIETY 1999 EXCLUSIVE

❑ #0126 Polar Bear with Polka Dot Collar

SPRING (MASS) 1998 SET

❑ #0127 Penguin in Chef's Hat

❑ #0131 Polar Bear in Argyle Shirt

❑ #0135 Walrus with Coca-Cola Bottle

❑ #0136 Husky with Coca-Cola Bottle

❑ #0137 Whale with Coca-Cola Bottle

❑ #0152 Reindeer with Coca-Cola Bottle

BLOCKBUSTER EXCLUSIVE CHRISTMAS 1997

❑ #0144 Polar Bear in Green Bow

❑ #0145 Seal in Green Scarf

❑ #0146 Polar Bear in Driver's Cap

❑ #0147 Seal in Long Stocking Cap

❑ #0148 Penguin in Snowflake Cap

❑ #0149 Polar Bear in Red Vest and Black Bowtie

CCCC SOCIETY EXCLUSIVE 1998

❑ #0151 Polar Bear in Green Sweater with Red Reindeer

WHITE'S GUIDE EXCLUSIVE KISSING BEARS 1997

❑ #0153 Polar Bear in Green Ribbon (girl)

❑ #0154 Polar Bear in Striped Scarf (boy)

COCA-COLA EXCLUSIVE PAIR 1998

❑ #0158 Seal in Tee Shirt (single "E" red tag)

❑ #0159 Polar Bear in Red Coca-Cola Snowflake Scarf
  (old face/single "E" red tag)
  (old face/double exclusive tag)
  (new face/double exclusive tag)

MEDIA PLAY EXCLUSIVE 1998

❑ #0161 Polar Bear in Cream & Green Checkered Shirt

❑ #0162 Reindeer w/ a Coca-Cola Holiday Shirt

❑ #0163 Polar Bear in Holiday Scarf

❑ #1064 Seal in Holiday Cap

POG EXCLUSIVE 1998

❑ #0165 Polar Bear in Blue/Green Checkered Vest

GCC EXCLUSIVE 1998

❑ #0166 Polar Bear in Blue Striped Delivery Suit

WINTER HERITAGE (GIFT) 1998

❑ #0167 Polar Bear in Checker Cap & Scarf

❑ #0168 Reindeer with Colorful Coca-Cola Vest & Hat

❑ #0169 Polar Bear in Blue Night Cap

❑ #0170 Seal in Delivery Outfit (blue)

❑ #0171 Polar Bear in Soda Fountain Outfit (red)

❑ #0172 Penguin in Holiday Vest

MANCHU WOK BEAR 1998

❑ #0177 Polar Bear in Red Satin Jacket
  American (single tag) edition
  Canadian (double tag) edition

2ND EDITION WHITE'S GUIDE KISSING BEARS 1998

❑ #0182 Polar Bear in Blue Bowtie and Vest (boy)

❑ #0183 Polar Bear in Red Bow and Jumper (girl)

COKE COLLECTORS CLASSIC EXCLUSIVE 1998

❑ #0184 Polar Bear in Collector Classic Tee Shirt

CARROWS RESTAURANT POLAR BEAR PAIR 1999

❑ #186 Polar Bear in Red Tank Top

❑ #187 Polar Bear in Red Striped Scarf

WORLD OF COCA-COLA STORE EXCLUSIVES 1998/1999

❑ #0191 Polar Bear in World of Coca-Cola

Atlanta Tee Shirt

(old face/single E tag)

(old face/double exclusive tags)

(new face/double exclusive tags)

❑ #0192 Polar Bear in World of Coca-Cola Las Vegas Tee Shirt

(old face/double exclusive tags)

(new face/double exclusive tags)

❑ #0270 Polar Bear in Everything Atlanta Tee Shirt

(new face/double exclusive tags)

❑ #0271 Polar Bear in Everything New York Tee Shirt

(new face/double exclusive tags)

COCA-COLA FORMAL PAIR 1998

❑ #0193 Polar Bear in Black Velvet Vest (boy)

❑ #0194 Polar Bear in Red Satin Collar & Bow (girl)

COCA-COLA EXCLUSIVE GIFT SET OF FOUR 1999

❑ #0195 Polar Bear in Holiday Pattern Vest (boy)

❑ #0196 Polar Bear in Jumper (girl)

❑ #0197 Seal in Nightshirt and Cap

❑ #0198 Polar Bear in Nightshirt and Cap

EVERYDAY (MASS) SET 1999

❑ #0199 Polar Bear in Plaid Baseball Cap

❑ #0200 Polar Bear in Blue Pattern Shirt

❑ #0201 Polar Bear in Plaid Scarf

❑ #0202 Penguin in Green Pattern Vest

❑ #0203 Seal in Green Pattern Scarf

❑ #0204 Seal in Blue Pattern Baseball Cap

WINTER (MASS) SET 1999

❑ #0205 Penguin in Striped Vest

❑ #0206 Polar Bear in Long Striped Cap

❑ #0207 Seal in Striped Vest and Knit Cap (Green)

❑ #0208 Polar Bear in Striped Vest and Bowtie

❑ #0209 Polar Bear in Striped Shirt and Bowtie

❑ #0210 Seal in Striped Scarf and Knit Cap (Red)

❑ WINTER SET 1999 ALBERTSONS DOUBLE EXCLUSIVE TAGS

❑ WINTER SET 1999 SAV-ON DOUBLE EXCLUSIVE TAGS

❑ WINTER SET 1999 LUCKY DOUBLE EXCLUSIVE TAGS

INTERNATIONAL BEAN BAG COLLECTION (1999)

SET 1

❑ #0211 Reegle, Eagle, United States

❑ #0212 Toolu, Toucan, Honduras

❑ #0213 Dover, Bulldog, Great Britain

❑ #0214 Strudel, Poodle, France

❑ #0215 Toro, Bull, Spain

❑ #0216 Curry, Bengal Tiger, India

❑ #0217 Clomp, Elephant, Kenya

❑ #0218 Rilly, Gorilla, Rwanda

❑ #0219 Masa, Lion, Mozambique

❑ #0220 Quala, Koala, Australia

SET 2

❑ #0221 Can Can, Pelican, Cuba

❑ #0222 Baltic, Reindeer, Sweden

- ❏ #0223 Paco, Iguana, Mexico
- ❏ #0224 Rifraff, Giraffe, Somalia
- ❏ #0225 Croon, Baboon, Pakistan
- ❏ #0226 Salty, Sea Turtle, Bahamas
- ❏ #0227 Vaca, Longhorn Cow, Argentina
- ❏ #0228 Zongshi, Panda, China
- ❏ #0229 Barrot, Parrot, Brazil
- ❏ #0230 Fannie, Fox, Germany

SET 3

- ❏ #0231 Taps, Tapir, Venezuela
- ❏ #0232 Rhiny, Black Rhinoceros, Tanzania
- ❏ #0233 Gourmand, Moose, Canada
- ❏ #0234 Lors, Wild Boar, Italy
- ❏ #0235 Barris, Brown Bear, Russia
- ❏ #0236 Waks, Yak, Nepal
- ❏ #0237 Key Key, Snow Monkey, Japan
- ❏ #0238 Ramel, Camel, Egypt
- ❏ #0239 Pock, Peacock, Sri Lanka
- ❏ #0240 Badgey, Badger, Czech Republic

SET 4

- ❏ #0241 Topus, Zebra, Nigeria
- ❏ #0242 Waller, Walrus, Greenland
- ❏ #0243 Laffs, Llama, Bolivia
- ❏ #0244 Woolsy, Sheep, Ireland
- ❏ #0245 Crunch, Crocodile, Sudan
- ❏ #0246 Howls, Wolf, Romania
- ❏ #0247 Orany, Orangutan, Singapore
- ❏ #0248 Ardie, Aardvark, Niger
- ❏ #0249 Heeta, Cheetah, Nambia
- ❏ #0250 Blubby, Pot Belly Pig, Vietnam

SET 5

- ❏ #0251 Hopps, Coki Frog, Puerto Rico
- ❏ #0252 Peng, Penguin, Chili
- ❏ #0253 Lochs, Rabbit, Scotland
- ❏ #0254 Neppy, Proboscis Monkey, Thailand

- ❏ #0255 Meeska, Hippopotamus, Zambia
- ❏ #0256 Nardie, St. Bernard, Switzerland
- ❏ #0257 Kelp, Kiwi, New Zealand
- ❏ #0258 Oppy, Octopus, Greece
- ❏ #0259 Streak, Jackal, Tunisia
- ❏ #0260 Masha, Ostrich, South Africa

**CAVANAGH COCA-COLA
CHRISTMAS SOCIETY EXCLUSIVE**

- ❏ #0268 Totonca, Buffalo, USA

SPORTING SET 1999

- ❏ #0261 Polar Bear in Baseball Jersey
- ❏ #0262 Polar Bear in Football Jersey
- ❏ #0263 Penguin in Hockey Sweater
- ❏ #0264 Polar Bear in Red Golf Shirt
- ❏ #0265 Polar Bear in Ski Outfit
- ❏ #0266 Seal in Soccer Shirt

GCC EXCLUSIVE 1999

- ❏ #0267 Polar Bear in Red Romper

COCA-COLA EXCLUSIVE SET OF FOUR 1999

- ❏ #0269 Polar Bear in Hooded Sweatshirt
  (Property of Coca-Cola)
- ❏ #0272 Red Coca-Cola Disk
- ❏ #0273 Seal in Delivery Outfit
- ❏ #0274 Polar Bear in Serving Jacket and Hat

YEAR 2000 SET

- ❏ #0277 Polar Bear in 2000 Top Hat (boy)
- ❏ #0278 Polar Bear in 2000 Vest (girl)
- ❏ #0279 Seal in 2000 Vest
- ❏ #0280 Penguin in 2000 Scarf

MEDIA PLAY/MUSICLAND EXCLUSIVE 1999

- #0287 Polar Bear in Red Soda Jerk Vest
- #0288 Polar Bear in Suspenders
- #0289 Polar Bear in Red Delivery Jacket

COKE COLLECTORS CLASSIC BEAR 1999

- #0304 1999 Collector Classic Polar Bear

CAREER SET 2000

- #0310 Polar Bear Fireman (boots, suspenders & hat)
- #0311 Polar Bear Construction Worker (overalls & cap)
- #0312 Reindeer Artist (jacket & beret)
- #0313 Seal Chef (apron & chef's hat)
- #0314 Penguin Pilot (scarf, aviator cap & goggles)
- #0315 Polar Bear Policeman (jacket & hat)

EVERYDAY (MASS) SET 2000

- #0316 Penguin in Soda Jerk Outfit
- #0317 Polar Bear in Soda Jerk Outfit
- #0318 Reindeer in Soda Jerk Outfit
- #0319 Polar Bear in Delivery Outfit with Cap
- #0320 Penguin in Delivery Outfit with Cap
- #0321 Seal in Delivery Outfit with Cap

ZOO ATLANTA PANDA BEARS 1999

- #0322 Exclusive Krogers/Zoo Atlanta Panda Bear
- #0323 Exclusive World of Coca-Cola Panda Bear

2ND EDITION INTERNATIONAL COLLECTION (2000)

GROUP 1

- #0330 Sailor, Swan, Austria
- #0333 Duckles, Mandarin Duck, Taiwan
- #0343 Fire, Flying Dragon, Indonesia
- #0345 Tides, Killer Whale, Norway
- #0351 Jose, Jaguar, Peru
- #0365 Crooner, Raccoon, USA

GROUP 2

- #0332 Mingo, Flamingo, Morocco
- #0339 Baccy, Hedgehog, Wales
- #0346 Anty, Anteater, Paraguay
- #0353 Apache, Wild Pony, USA
- #0354 Lammer, Lammergeier, Ukraine
- #0357 Ringer, Small Spotted Genet, Portugal

GROUP 3

- #0341 Odes, Skunk, USA
- #0342 Cockles, Rooster, Malaysia
- #0344 Shep, Mouflon Sheep, Slovakia
- #0358 Cawcaw, Scarlet Macaw, Columbia
- #0363 Hans, White Stork, Netherlands
- #0364 Otties, River Otter, Poland

GROUP 4

- #0334 Freddie, Flying Squirrel, Zaire
- #0335 Grizzy, Grizzly Bear, USA
- #0336 Batts, Fruit Bat, Angola
- #0338 Hooty, Northern Hawk Owl, Lithuania
- #0350 Whitey, Arctic Fox, Finland
- #0356 Eire, Puffin, Northern Ireland

CAVANAGH COCA-COLA CHRISTMAS SOCIETY 2000 EXCLUSIVES

- #0347 Gator the Alligator, USA
- #0367 Possy the Opossum, USA

MISCELLANEOUS EDITIONS

UNNUMBERED CAVANAGH-PRODUCED EDITIONS

❏ McDonald's Owners Convention 1998 Boy and Girl Polar Bears w/out numbers

❏ Thanks a Billion Bear 1998

❏ McDonald's Operations Boston Region Polar Bear 1999

MINI COLLECTIBLE EDITIONS

❏ #0205 Mini Polar Bear with Watch

❏ #0213 Eat 'n Park Penguin

NASCAR DRIVER BEARS 1999

❏ #18 Bobby Labonte

❏ #20 Tony Stewart

❏ #28 Kenny Irwin

❏ #44 Kyle Petty

❏ #45 Adam Petty

❏ #88 Dale Jarrett

❏ #94 Bill Elliott

❏ #99 Jeff Burton

NASCAR DRIVER BEARS 2000

❏ #1 Steve Park

❏ #3 Dale Earnhardt Sr.

❏ #8 Dale Earnhardt Jr.

❏ #18 Bobby Labonte

❏ #20 Tony Stewart

❏ #44 Kyle Petty

❏ #88 Dale Jarrett

❏ #94 Bill Elliott

❏ #99 Jeff Burton

MARY MEYERS RACERS

❏ RedLiners Earnhardt Sr.

❏ RedLiners Earnhardt Jr.

SPORTS EDITIONS

❏ 1998 Kentucky Wildcats Bean Bag

❏ 1999 Brutus Buckeye Bean Bag

COLLECTOR CLUB EDITIONS

❏ 1997 Atlanta Chapter TCCCC Christmas Party Moose

❏ 1998 Springtime in Atlanta Moose

❏ 1998 Minneapolis TCCCC Annual Convention Frog

❏ 1998 Atlanta Chapter TCCCC Christmas Party Ty Deer

❏ 1999 Ohio Winterfest TCCCC Bear (numbered)

❏ 1999 Springtime in Atlanta Bunny

❏ 1999 Badger Chapter TCCCC Spring Pause Cow

❏ 1999 Sun n' Fun Millennium Bash Bear

❏ 1999 Dallas 25th Anniversary Convention Horse

❏ 1999 Virginia Beach Party Dolphin

❏ 1999 Choo-Choo Chapter TCCCC Dalmatian

❏ 1999 NW Georgia TCCCC Merry Christmas Party Cat

❏ 1999 Atlanta TCCCC Christmas Pink Pig

❏ 1999 Ohio Valley Chapter TCCCC 19th Christmas Party Monkey

❏ 1999 Choo-Choo TCCCC Christmas Party Squirrel

❏ 2000 Ohio Winterfest TCCCC Mouse

INTERNATIONAL EDITIONS

AUSTRALIA/NEW ZEALAND

1997 Australian Hungry Jacks Buddy Bears

❏ Polar Bear with Red Bow

❏ Polar Bear with Red Fringed Scarf

1998 New Zealand Burger King Buddy Bears
❑ Polar Bear with Plaid Ribbon
❑ Polar Bear with Plaid Bowtie
❑ Polar Bear with Red Vest
❑ Polar Bear with Red Scarf

1998 Village Cinema Bears
❑ Bubbles (boy bear with plaid bowtie)
❑ Fizz (girl bear with plaid bow)

1998 Australian Kmart Set of Four
❑ Seal in Baseball Cap
❑ Penguin in Delivery Cap
❑ Polar Bear in Red Baseball Cap
❑ Polar Bear in Red Shirt

1999 Chinese New Year Bunnies (set of four)
❑ Bunny in Red Vest
❑ Bunny in Red Scarf
❑ Bunny in Red Pants
❑ Bunny with Ball

1999 AUSTRALIAN CHRISTMAS SET OF FOUR
❑ Penguin with Red Ribbon
❑ Seal with Red Cap and Red Ribbon
❑ Reindeer with Red Ribbon
❑ Polar Bear with Red Bow and Ribbon

❑ 1999   AMF Australian Bowler Bear

2000 AUSTRALIAN FOOTBALL LEAGUE BEARS
❑ Adelaide Crows
❑ Brisbane Lions
❑ Carlton Blues
❑ Collingwood Magpies
❑ Essendon Bombers
❑ Footscray Western Bulldogs
❑ Fremantle Dockers
❑ GeeLong Cats
❑ Hawthorn Hawks

❑ Melbourne Demons
❑ North Melbourne Kangaroos
❑ Port Adelaide Port Power
❑ Richmond Tigers
❑ Saint Kilda Saints
❑ Sydney Swans
❑ West Coast Eagles

EUROPEAN EDITIONS
❑ 1998   English Coke Can
❑ 1999   German Polar Bear in a Can
❑ 1999   German Trink Bear
❑ 1999   English Mickey Coke Bean Bag
❑ 1999   English Polar Bear
❑ 1999   English Burger King Polar Bear
❑ 1999   German Penguin with Scarf & Cap
❑ 1999   German Summer Set
❑ 1999   German Polar Bear in a Can
    2nd Edition

2000 GERMAN SET OF 8
❑ Polar Bear with Scarf
❑ Polar Bear with Bowtie
❑ Polar Bear with Bottle
❑ Penguin with Chef's Hat
❑ Penguin with Scarf
❑ Seal with Scarf
❑ Seal with Life Preserver
❑ Polar Bear with Red Scarf

ASIAN EDITIONS
1999 Hong Kong Family of Four Bears
❑ PaPa
❑ MaMa
❑ CoCo
❑ LaLa

❑ 1999 Hong Kong Polar Bear in Red Scarf

Resource List

THE COCA-COLA COMPANY

1-800-GET-COKE   (Consumer Affairs)

or visit The Company website at:

http://www.cocacola.com

COCA-COLA STORE CONTACT INFORMATION:

WORLD OF COCA-COLA ATLANTA

55 Martin Luther King Drive

Atlanta, GA 30303

800-676-2653

EVERYTHING COCA-COLA LAS VEGAS

3785 Las Vegas Blvd. South

Las Vegas, NV 89109

800-810-2653

EVERYTHING COCA-COLA STORE

Hartsfield International Airport

6000 South Terminal Parkway

(across from security check-in)

Atlanta, GA

404-763-3166

**CAVANAGH COCA-COLA
COLLECTORS SOCIETY:**

P.O. Box 768090

Roswell, GA 30076

800-653-1221

EMAIL:

ccccs@cavanaghgrp.com

OR VISIT THE WEBSITE AT:

http://www.cavanaghgrp.com

THE COCA-COLA COLLECTORS CLUB

Membership in the club is $30 U.S., $35 Canada or $50 overseas. There are many local and state chapters you can also join. For more information, contact:

The Coca-Cola Collectors Club

PMB 609, 4780 Ashford Dunwoody Rd #A

Atlanta, GA 30338

Or visit the Website at:

http://www.cocacolaclub.org

WEBSITE LISTING COCA-COLA BEAN BAGS:

(updated weekly)

http://www.4beanies-cola.com/beanbaglist.html

Satisfy Your Thirst For
COKE® COLLECTIBLES.

The Officially Licensed
Coca-Cola Collectibles Books From Beckett®.

ISBN: 1-887432-93-0
160 pages
$24.95

COCA-COLA® *Collectible Santas*

The COCA-COLA® Santa is a familiar figure during the holiday season. This wonderful book features a history and current secondary market pricing for these traditional festive collectibles. Includes COCA-COLA® Sundblom art, print advertising, trays, bottles/cans, signage, figures, pins, plush and much more.

ISBN: 1-887432-99-X
160 pages
$24.95

COCA-COLA® *Collectible Cars & Trucks*

Noted COCA-COLA® collector Kyle Foreman helped put together this fun book covering vintage and modern COCA-COLA®-themed cars and trucks. Contains a history and secondary market pricing for cars, trucks, trains and other vehicles. NASCAR-licensed cars, international productions, airplanes, models and kits are also included.

ISBN: 1-887432-92-2
160 pages
$24.95

COCA-COLA® *Collectible Polar Bears*

The COKE® Polar Bears from the popular advertising campaign are featured in this marvelous book. Features a complete history, plus secondary market pricing for collectibles from the ad campaign, including trays, bottles/cans, pins, figures, bean bags and plush.

ISBN: 1-887432-97-3
160 pages
$24.95

COCA-COLA® *Collectible Bean Bags & Plush*

Respected COCA-COLA® collectors Linda Lee Harry and Suzi Harry authored this comprehensive guide to COCA-COLA® bean bag and plush toys. Features a complete history and secondary market pricing for the popular collectibles - both domestic and international. Includes Cavanaugh plush, some limited-edition special event issues and much more.

Presented By:

Collect all four of these popular collectibles price guides.

Note: Book covers shown may change upon shipment.